Breaking t

The Suffragette Story in North Devon

Pamela Vass

Boundstone Books

First published in Great Britain in 2017 by Boundstone Books, Little Boundstone, Littleham, Bideford. EX39 5HW.

ISBN: 978-0-9568709-6-4

Printed and bound in Great Britain by SRP, Exeter.

www.boundstonebooks.co.uk

Also by this author

Fiction

Seeds of Doubt
Shadow Chid

Non-Fiction

The Power of Three
On Course for Recovery

Edited works

In My Own Words

Acknowledgements

I am grateful to the following individuals and institutions for access to their archives, for the knowledge they have generously shared with me and for their ongoing support.

Margaret Atherton; Peter Christie; Beverley Cook, Museum of London; Charles Payne; Mary Evans Picture library; Women's Library, LSE; British Library; North Devon Record Office; Westcountry Studies Library; Bideford & District Archive; Ilfracombe Museum; Dr Pip Jollands; Alison Harding; Liz Shakespeare; Ben Shakespeare; Laurence Shelley and Terence Sackett.

Author's Note

Breaking the Mould is the result of extensive research through suffrage and local newspapers and the accounts of the lives of those pivotal to the suffragette and suffragist movements. Some scenes are imagined, however all dates and details are accurate and reflect the story of the fight for the vote in North Devon and beyond.

Contents

Prologue

Ilfracombe, Devon
March 1912

They stand in silence waiting for the London Express. Katherine Marie Anstis du Sautoy Newby draws her overcoat closer around her slim frame as the biting sea air sweeps across the platform at Ilfracombe station. Her husband Dr Newby stands beside her, grasping her arm just a little tighter than necessary. How easy it would be to return to their homely villa in Broad Park Avenue. Easy, but not an option, not this time.

Marie checks her portmanteau. Cotton wool, newspaper, small stones, identification, a change of dress, the bare essentials. 'I've left menus with Elizabeth,' she says, anxious to break the silence between them. 'You just need to give her your schedule each week. And Elsie will attend to any household matters.'

'I'll be perfectly well taken care of. I just wish I could say the same of you.' He squeezes her hand discreetly.

They said their farewells in the privacy of the drawing room but his touch is reassuring. There's no turning back, Marie knows that, but she shivers at the prospect of what lies ahead. It's one thing to read in the newspapers of the appalling brutality towards women, but soon she will be standing shoulder to shoulder with them. No-one knows what will happen then, not even Mrs Pankhurst.

Chapter One
A Pankhurst in Ilfracombe
January 1909

Ilfracombe, North Devon. Marie is late. She hurries through streets unusually busy for a dark January night; not with couples out for an evening stroll or families returning home, but women, hundreds of them, streaming towards the Runnacleave Hotel. She's tempted to turn back. The hall might be full. No point squeezing herself in at the back where she'll not hear anything. Besides, there's more than enough to get on with at home.

'Marie.' A voice calls from behind. Marie hesitates, only to be buffeted by women pushing past. 'Glad I've caught up with you.' Anne Ball tucks her arm through Marie's. 'We can go in together, bit of Dutch courage.'

'I was just thinking … if it's going to be busy …'

'Brilliant isn't it? Not every day we get a militant here, so I'm not surprised. Come on.' There was no arguing with Anne Ball when she set her mind to something. Probably why she made such a good superintendent of the Ilfracombe Trained Nurses Institute and another in Barnstaple. She was made for business, as well as being an excellent nurse.

They hurry on, heads bent against the wind driving around Capstone Hill. It's the YMCA's first debate of the year and the organisers have lured Annie Kenney, one of the new breed of militant suffragettes, to this rural outpost. The papers have christened her 'The Oldham Firebrand' for her fearless heckling of politicians and Parliament. Not to mention her orchestration of the mass marches and street protests that inevitably end in scuffles with the police and undignified arrests. It promises to be a good night.

They join the queue filtering through the conservatory entrance. 'Oh,' Marie exclaims, pointing to a notice displayed in the foyer. 'Miss Adela Pankhurst replaces Miss Annie Kenney for this evening's debate.'

'Would have been good to hear Annie but think about it, an actual Pankhurst, here in Ilfracombe!' Anne is irrepressible. 'I mean, the Pankhursts are forever making headlines up country but can you ever remember one coming here?' She presses ahead into the cavernous hall that reeks of faded elegance. Mahogany panels frame enormous arched windows, obscured by folds of velvet drapes.

'But who is Adela Pankhurst?' Marie asks as Anne leads the way to some vacant seats near the front. 'I've heard of Christabel, even Sylvia, but Adela?'

A party of men and one woman climbs the wooden steps to the stage. 'That must be her,' Anne whispers.

It would be easy to be underwhelmed by Adela Pankhurst, barely five feet tall, slender and so nervous you'd think there was a price on her head. Nothing like the Amazon many might expect given press coverage of the Pankhursts.

VOTES FOR WOMEN.

Miss ADELA PANKHURST,

Organiser, National Women's Social and Political Union, 4, Clement's Inn, Strand, W.C.

The chairman steps forward. 'The question of woman suffrage is very much to the fore just now and demands serious consideration. Miss Adela Pankhurst will speak for the motion, Mr Blackmore against.'

Adela glances nervously round the hall then steps to the front of the stage. 'Ladies and gentlemen, I'm here to propose that the Parliamentary Franchise should be granted to women on the same terms as men.'

'What's a Parliamentary Franchise?' Marie whispers.

'The Vote.'

'Men have won their liberty,' Adela continues. 'No taxes are imposed or laws made except by their direct representatives in the Commons. But women are excluded from such privilege. They also pay taxes but have no voice in how those taxes are spent.' Murmurs and mutterings follow every statement, with more than a little heckling from the men.

'The anti-Suffragettes say a woman's place is at home. They claim home would be neglected if women had Parliamentary duties. Well, women who have the municipal vote wash up, sew buttons on and cook dinner just as well.'

Laughter ripples across the hall - women's laughter.

'Criminals, lunatics, paupers - and women have no vote. Is it not high time to lift us out of such company.' (Laughter and cheers.)

Mr Blackmore takes centre stage. 'The course proposed by Miss Pankhurst would lead to national disaster! Where is the evidence that the vote is wanted by more than a noisy handful of women? It is too great a sacrifice to gain the Parliamentary vote at the cost of our home life. Women are by nature unfitted for politics: their influence in the proper sphere will be greater without the franchise.'

The chairman has to shout over the bedlam. 'I would remind you,' he strains, 'that it is our tradition to give each speaker a fair hearing. I now open the debate to the floor.'

Arguments for and against rattle across the room until the chairman calls for the speakers to sum up. Adela stands. 'My opponents have made up their speeches before the meeting and have answered none of my arguments. (Laughter.) In Australia and New Zealand as soon as women had the vote men asked what they wanted.'

Marie gasps as the news sinks in. Britain ruled the Empire yet two of her territories had already given women the vote! If there, why not here?

Adela continues. 'Women care for their children but no woman has a right to her child after it is seven years old. The law then recognises but one parent, the man! Let women have the vote to shape the law.' (Applause and cheers) Marie shudders. To have no say in her daughter's life. It was unthinkable.

'We'll move to a vote,' the chairman announces. 'Those for?' He pauses as the tellers work their way down the rows. 'Those against?' Another rustling as arms are raised. But Marie's hands stay clenched in her lap. So much she has heard this evening has shocked and angered her, but to associate herself with women who commit criminal acts serious enough to put them in prison! It was a step too far - for now. She waits as the clerk hands the Chairman a piece of paper.

'On the Resolution that the Parliamentary Franchise be granted to women the voting is as follows.' He pauses for effect. 'For the motion, 114 Against, 115.'

'You see the difference one vote can make,' Anne says.

Marie Newby was a respected figure within Ilfracombe. From her elegant semi-detached villa in Broad Park Avenue she supported her husband Charles, a distinguished surgeon, and played her part at charitable functions within the church and town. Alongside Marie at the Runnacleave Hall was someone who was to become her partner in crime, Nurse Anne Ball, an independent businesswoman responsible for two Trained Nurses Institutes, one at Larkstone Terrace, Ilfracombe, and the other in Ashleigh Road, Barnstaple. Between them they were to galvanise local women in a focused campaign for the vote, embracing militancy along the way. But on the evening of Adela Pankhurst's talk they were merely dipping their toes in the water.

Very little had happened in North Devon for almost thirty years before the YMCA livened things up with their debate. At a second in Barnstaple, Mr Rowe, the Conservative agent and convincing advocate for the women's cause, dropped his bombshell: 'Before 1832 there was nothing in any Franchise Act that prevented women from voting. It was only when they tried to claim their vote that judges ruled a woman was legally incapacitated by her sex from doing so.' Men and women might have equal duties and obligations, but any rights and privileges were reserved for men. The rights of half the nation were extinguished at a stroke!

Mr Rowe's speech was punctuated with positive arguments for change in support of the women. 'Those who have to obey the laws should have a voice in making them ... Taxation and representation should go hand in hand ... Women share the responsibility of managing cities and boroughs, choosing Parliamentary representatives needs no greater wisdom ... It's impossible for a council of wise men to legislate on questions concerning women without the assistance and guidance of that sex ... How much longer can this absurd condition exist?'

How much longer indeed? It was a persuasive argument.

Mr Rowe moved to the climax of his speech: 'The spirit of justice and freedom will continue to triumph until the slavery of sex has followed that of caste, colour and race and woman, no longer the chattel of man, has taken her just place as his helpmate, companion, friend - with no rivalry between them, but that of noble thought and noble deed.' Marie and Anne joined in the thunderous applause for Mr Rowe. There really was no argument against giving women the vote.

The next speaker, Mr Copp, begged to differ, airing entrenched views the women were to hear time and time again: 'There is a danger the easy-going public will drift into female suffrage with the indifference born of familiarity. (Laughter) ... Women have done admirable work on Local Government bodies because they are within their rightful province. The extension of the franchise would place a burden on them for which they have neither capacity nor leisure ... Voters moved chiefly by sentiment would be a great menace to the equilibrium of national politics ... It is desirable that women should devote themselves to work other than political, their mental and moral development fitting them for a better fate.' Mr Copp concluded, 'Strive to be none other than you are, but to be that other well.' (Laughter and applause.)

The chairman opened up the debate to the floor. Perhaps surprisingly, the first speakers, all male, were not won over by Mr Copp's arguments and spoke in support of the women: 'Ladies are perfectly able to cope with any legislative matters they come into contact with.' (Applause) ... 'Ladies are the victims of convention which is unfair to the Ladies themselves.' (Hear, hear) ... 'There is no sound argument to be brought against Women's Suffrage'... 'What's sauce for the goose is sauce for the gander, and the women who pay the piper should be given an opportunity of selecting the tune.' (Loud laughter)

Then, for the first time, a woman stood. Miss Kate James: (Cheers) 'I would not like to go away thinking no woman was prepared to speak in favour of the extension of the Parliamentary Franchise to women. (Hear, hear) ... Does Mr Copp know that eighty-two percent of the women of this country have to work for themselves, for their children, for their parents, crippled children and drunken husbands? (Shame!) ... It is time we had a right to vote.' (Cheers)

After concluding comments, the Chairman moved to the vote: 'Those in favour of the Parliamentary Franchise being granted to women.' A forest of hands filled the room. 'Thank you. The motion is passed by an overwhelming majority.'

In other parts of the country debate had already given way to action. Women were finding their political voice, confusing the male-dominated political world. What on earth was driving respectable women to dare to interrupt speakers at political meetings? They embarrassed themselves as much as others by acting in such an unladylike way. And as for their mass marches on the House of Commons, well, it couldn't be helped if some were determined to make martyrs of themselves and end up in prison. They should stick to expressing their views as they had for years, with polite conversation and perhaps the occasional petition.

Women had tried polite conversation and the occasional petition for over fifty years. Devon alone sent 253 petitions to Parliament with a national one, in 1896, signed by a quarter of a million women. There had been over 50,000 meetings, marches and rallies in the five years leading up to 1909, demonstrating massive support for change. But no amount of polite lobbying from the only suffrage organisation at the time, the National Union of Women's Suffrage Societies (NUWSS) made the slightest difference. It was business as usual in the exclusively male House of Commons with MPs refusing to pass any Bills on Woman Suffrage.

One woman was about to turn this polite lobbying on its head. Emmeline Pankhurst had campaigning in her blood. As a child she was bathed in arguments for women's suffrage from her feminist mother and her equally pro-suffrage father. She even chose a husband who was a keen advocate of women's rights.

For years she worked within the polite and law abiding NUWSS, but by 1903 it was obvious to Emmeline that the polite approach had failed. It was time to honour her family heritage and take centre stage: 'In spite of the overwhelming demand which women have shown for the possession of the Parliamentary vote, in spite of the fact that every consideration of justice points to their right to possess it, the franchise has not been conceded, and in consequence women have found it necessary to take more vigorous measures.' For Emmeline and her daughters, Christabel, Sylvia and Adela, this meant breaking away from the NUWSS to form the Women's Social and Political Union (WSPU), a new group with a new slogan: Deeds not Words. Out with polite petitions. In with direct action.

The WSPU grew rapidly, appointing regional organisers with the courage, eloquence and ability to galvanise crowds. The person destined to lead the campaign in the West Country had all of those qualities and more. She was Annie Kenney, the Oldham firebrand.

Annie began her working life aged ten in a cotton mill. The noise, dirt and drudgery defeated many, but Annie was a fighter. Fascinated with politics she joined the local branch of the Independent Labour Party where she heard Christabel Pankhurst speak on women's rights. Annie fell under Christabel's spell, surrendering herself to the cause. She spoke of the militant movement as: 'more like a religious revival than a political movement. It stirred the emotions, it aroused passions, it awakened the human chord which responds to the battle-call of freedom...' She offered loyalty and an unselfish devotion to the cause. And for Annie this meant giving herself mind, body and soul to Christabel.

Sylvia Pankhurst described Annie as: '... eager and impulsive in manner, with a thin, haggard face, and restless knotted hands, from one of which a finger had been torn by the machinery it was her work to attend. Her abundant, loosely dressed golden hair was the most youthful looking thing about her ... The wild, distraught expression, apt to occasion solicitude, was found on better acquaintance to be less common than a bubbling merriment, in which the crow's feet wrinkled quaintly about a pair of twinkling, bright blue eyes.'

Those twinkling blue eyes exuded a charisma that drew women to her. Annie's passion for justice and women's rights was matched by her passion for the women she came to know. Relationships blurred as campaign alliances became entangled with emotional attachments, often observed by supporter, Mary Blathwayt. Mary's home, Eagle House near Bath, was a place of respite for many suffragettes over the years, including Annie, whose activities are mentioned frequently in Mary's diary. *'Annie slept with someone else again last night.' 'There was someone else in Annie's bed this morning'.*

The first and most intense of these relationships was with Christabel herself. Christabel was beautiful, intelligent, graceful, confident, charming, charismatic - and with a track record for close relationships with other women. But this was a naive time. 'Close' relationships between women, even when they involved sharing beds, weren't seen as out of the ordinary. Annie admitted suffragettes developed a different set of values to other women: 'The changed life into which most of us entered was a revolution in itself. No home life, no-one to say what we should do or what we should not do, no family ties, we were free and alone in a great brilliant city, scores of young women scarcely out of their teens met together in a revolutionary movement, outlaws or

breakers of laws, independent of everything and everybody, fearless and self-confident.'

That fearlessness was on show on October 13th, 1905 when Annie and Christabel joined the crowds at Manchester's Free Trade Hall determined to heckle Sir Edward Grey, a potential cabinet minister. He was appealing for the return of a Liberal Government when they thrust a white banner into the air. 'Votes for Women' it proclaimed. Annie called: 'If you are elected, will you do your best to make Woman Suffrage a Government Measure?' She was ignored. She stood again, but was immediately pulled down by men in the crowd. Christabel repeated the question unleashing a hubbub of mixed cries from, 'shut up,' to, 'let the lady speak.'

Eventually they were dragged from the meeting. During the scuffle a policeman accused them of kicking and spitting which, of course, they did. It was a deliberate ploy by Christabel to get arrested. They were charged with assault and appeared in court the next day. But far from being cowed, they were triumphant. Christabel had declared war. They refused to pay any fines and were sentenced to three days' imprisonment. It was unprecedented. For the first time in Britain, women had used violence in an attempt to win the vote. As far as the Daily Mail was concerned a new breed of suffragists had been born: suffragettes.

For Annie, it was a turning point. Christabel had lit a fire that led her to a land of political freedom. She never returned to the mill, taking instantly to the public platform, commanding crowds with her powerful voice and expressive language. Their movement would have to break through the old guard's rock-solid belief that a woman's place was in the home, but she was convinced the WSPU would triumph.

In 1907, Devon experienced Annie's revolutionary zeal at first hand when she was appointed WSPU organiser for the West Country, working out of headquarters in Bristol. She identified the forthcoming Mid Devon by-election as a prime target for action. Standing side-by-side with Emmeline Pankhurst she campaigned against the Liberal candidate. It was an ambitious strategy. There had been seven elections in the constituency since 1885 with a Liberal returned each and every time, on the last occasion with a majority of well over a thousand. But Mrs Pankhurst was undaunted. The Liberal Government was imprisoning and torturing hundreds of women. She would do her utmost to unseat every candidate that stood for the party to protest at this injustice.

Annie organised a ferocious programme of public meetings, contending not only with heavy snow and bitter winds but tempestuous locals. The window of their committee room in Newton Abbot was smashed, meetings disrupted and a wagon they were speaking from almost overturned. But they were undeterred. On a typical day they held six or more meetings across the area, from Teignmouth to Chagford, Bovey Tracey to Ashburton, attracting crowds of up to 500.

Amy Montague from Crediton was a stalwart supporter, chairing meetings and even composing an anthem to compete with the Liberals election songs.

Mrs Pankhurst's bravado in the face of local gangs was almost her undoing. When it was announced that the Conservative had won, the police urged her to leave town at once. She laughed at such an absurd warning - until confronted by a mob of young men, clay cutters, all wearing the Liberal red rosettes. A shower of rotten eggs and clay balls sent the women rushing into a grocer's shop. They tried to escape through the back but the gang outmanoeuvred them. Mrs Pankhurst was hit on the head, seized and flung to the ground. The gang of youths closed in but fortunately scattered at the first sign of the police. Her immediate ordeal was over but her injuries plagued her for more than a year.

At times she must have felt it was all for nothing. The Conservatives claimed they alone had kept the Liberals out, while the Liberals blamed their defeat on Conservative promises of more work and higher wages. The *Manchester Guardian* was the only paper to report the truth. The suffragettes had overturned a Liberal majority of over a thousand.

Mrs Pankhurst was back in Devon in February 1909. *Votes for Women,* the suffragette paper, urged: 'If any readers of this paper have friends living in Devonshire, would they kindly write and advise them to seize the opportunity now before them to hear Mrs Pankhurst.' Women walked the streets selling the paper, a shocking sight in itself. Respectable women acting as common street sellers! It was unheard of. Yet that's exactly what they did, tirelessly publicising meetings in Paignton, Totnes, Teignmouth and more: 'Open air meetings are being held in all the surrounding districts and great numbers of handbills are being distributed. On Monday, Dartmouth was for the first time visited by workers of the WSPU when Miss Elsie Ball and Miss Mary Mills held a splendid open-air meeting. Over 400 people listened most attentively and a good collection was made.'

Mrs Pankhurst's first engagement was to a packed house at the Bath Saloon in Torquay. Every detail was thought of, right down to her bouquet - themed in green, white and violet, the colours of the WSPU. Emmeline Pankhurst set out her stall with stunning eloquence. She defended tactics that had made it impossible for any Cabinet Minister to address a public meeting without being surrounded by police. But most of all, it was a rallying call to action that rang round the Bath Saloon that night and again the following Wednesday at Plymouth Guildhall. What part, she asked, were those present going to take in the struggle for the freedom of their sex?

Mrs Pankhurst and her WSPU followers had been delivering speeches like this across the country for more than four years, building an impact way above their numbers. She launched a series of Women's Parliaments where the language was of rebellion. Speeches would end, 'To arms! The call to battle has gone forth'. Women responded, following their leader in public protests outside the House of Commons. It was an astonishing initiative that initially left the police wrong-footed. After all, convention dictated a deference to the ladies. But these were no Ladies. Police surrounded them on foot and horseback. Women were jeered at and, when they failed to see reason, physically assaulted. Instead of a hearing, women who went peacefully to the House of Commons risked being battered and abused. Elderly grandmothers were manhandled and publicly shamed in the streets with their underclothes pulled up over their heads. Those who wouldn't give up were hauled off to court and sentenced to months in Holloway, subjected to the worst possible conditions.

It was a massive wake-up call for Marie Newby and Anne Ball. It wasn't just criminals who were imprisoned but ordinary, respectable women who simply wanted to petition their elected - not by them of course - representatives in Parliament. How could that be a crime? Mrs Pankhurst wrote: 'Those women... were prepared to do something that women had never done before - fight for themselves. Women had always fought for men, and for their children. Now they were ready to fight for their own human rights. Our militant movement was established.'

But where Mrs Pankhurst saw courage, others recoiled from the women's actions. Anti-suffrage groups sprang up across the country, instigated by women determined to remain in their rightful place, behind their man. Men thought the whole suffrage thing a fad and were convinced that the little ladies would soon give up and go away. But once proved wrong they began to mobilise alongside the anti-suffrage ladies, playing the militants at their own game producing anti-suffrage cartoons and memorabilia.

THE ANTI-SUFFRAGE SOCIETY AS PORTRAIT-PAINTER

"THE A·S·S· — "This, my dear Mrs Britannia, is a true & authentic portrait of yourself if ever you get the vote."

Published by the Suffrage Atelier.

At the end of February 1909, Sir Thomas Acland, a familiar figure in Devon, presided at a meeting in Exeter of the National Women's Anti-Suffrage League. The question under debate was whether the Parliamentary Franchise should be extended to women. Countess Fortescue, a member of another prestigious Devon family, wrote: 'I must say it was not until recently I was fully able to make up my mind on the subject of women and the Suffrage. But now women have shown how totally unfit they are to take such heavy responsibilities on themselves, and I feel it will be an evil day when they become voters ...'

Annie Kenney's response was to redouble her efforts to convert hearts and minds in the West Country through an exhausting programme of public meetings and street canvassing. Alongside paid organisers Elsie Howey and Vera Wentworth, she ensured the WSPU's message reached women in Plymouth, Torquay, Dartmouth, Paignton, Totnes, Teignmouth, and down into Cornwall. Over six hundred turned out for a meeting in Penzance, with many more crowded outside.

It was against this backdrop that Adela Pankhurst arrived in Ilfracombe in January 1909. For the first time, women in North Devon had a focus for a sense of injustice that had been fermenting for years. It would take enormous courage to break aside from convention, especially for women of position such as Marie Newby and Anne Ball, but the WSPU was about to offer a familiar, if unusual inroad to activism ...

'It made no difference you know, what happened at mid-Devon.' Anne Ball was poring over her copy of 'Votes for Women', surrounded by Marie Newby and a small group of like-minded women. 'Asquith won't introduce a Suffrage Bill. Christabel is incensed. She and Mrs P. have called a war council.'

'They didn't call it that, surely,' Marie says.

'Sent shivers down my spine too. But Christabel says women are being defrauded, insulted, and dishonoured; that it's time to demand a Bill giving women taxpayers the vote. Why should women pay taxes if we have no say in how they are spent?'

'But if it means taking to the streets ... I couldn't possibly be one of those women ... to be locked up with common criminals! Look,' she grabs the paper from Anne. 'It says here the ladies who followed Mrs P. to protest

outside Parliament were surrounded by police, jeered at, manhandled, beaten, abused. Then forced to suffer the indignity of being brought before court. Fifty-nine arrests, and confined as ordinary second class prisoners in Holloway.' She shudders.

'They somehow found the courage,' Anne says quietly. 'They are all respectable women like us who simply want to have a voice.'

'I know,' Marie sighs. 'I know we have to do something. But not that, not yet. What else can we do?'

Anne smiles. 'Sew.'

'Sew!'

'Well, we look like a ladies' sewing circle so what else should we do to support the cause? The WSPU is looking for contributions for a Great Exhibition. Apparently no-one is too poor, too old, too young or too frail to do something. So no excuses, ladies!'

'What kind of Great Exhibition?'

'All the talk is of a sale of women's work that is so interesting, original and picturesque it will open the public's eyes to what the WSPU are capable of. It's to be held at the Princes Skating Rink in Knightsbridge and everything has to be in the colours for impact - purple, white and green. The Actresses Franchise League are providing entertainment and the women writers and artists have promised work. They want to sign up thousands of visitors to the cause. Oh, and the small matter of £5,000 to be raised for the campaign fund.'

'£5,000!' Margaret Eldridge exclaims. 'How will they raise that?'

'A hundred stalls taken by individuals, groups, societies, anyone basically who will undertake to supply items to the value of £100.'

'We can't possibly do that. And we're not even a proper group.'

'They've thought of that. As individual members we're urged to take a half, a quarter… even a twentieth of a stall run by a group near us. Are we agreed?'

A ripple of nods spreads around the room.

'And now you have to listen to this.' Anne peers at an article in 'Votes for Women'. 'There's a new post office regulation which allows the posting and delivery of human letters…'

'April 1st is it?' The women laugh.

'No … listen. A suffragette went to the West Strand Post Office with two women. "I want to send a human letter," she said. She took the official form they gave her and addressed her two companions to H. H. Asquith, 10

Downing Street. She paid the threepenny fee and delivered the women to a telegraph messenger with the instruction that they must be signed for on delivery. You should have seen it, the lad marched off towards Whitehall with a suffragette on each arm.'

'Priceless! What happened?'

'They were refused of course. But I'd loved to have seen the look on Asquith's face.'

The suffragettes' next attempt to engineer a close encounter with Asquith, this time in North Devon, was to be more successful.

Chapter Two
Outrage at Covelly Court
May 1909

Whit weekend at the end of May 1909. The crowds are gathering along the quay at Bideford, a historic North Devon port affectionately known as the little white town. It has a proud history of arrivals and departures. The incursions of Hubba the Dane are the stuff of legend, while Sir Richard Grenville sailed from the port to become the first Englishman to settle North America.

Today's arrival is no less exciting. The Prime Minister and his wife are expected at Bideford station en route to Clovelly Court. It's why Marie Newby and Anne Ball are also hurrying towards the bridge over the wide river to the station at East-the-Water.

'Will you join us?' Marie glances nervously at her husband sitting beside her in the car. His knuckles are white as he grips the steering wheel, his gaze fixed on the River Torridge.

'I would welcome the opportunity to shake our Prime Minister by the hand but do not wish to be associated with anything Nurse Ball may have in mind.' He nods at Anne pacing the quayside.

'She speaks her mind a little too often. I'm sure it was nothing more than rash words.'

'Rash words! Calling him the Right Dishonourable double-faced Asquith!'

'I know you don't approve of our meetings, but she wouldn't do anything... anything untoward.'

'I strongly advise you to stay with me, Marie. You see how the newspapers speak of these suffragettes. I will not have my wife tarred with the same brush.'

'Tarred with the same...! For years I have done everything in my power to support you, in your career, at home, in the town. Everything. And now you are forbidding me to go? When all I want is to catch sight of the man who seems resolved to throw every obstacle he can in the way of granting women the same choices in their own lives? If you are so opposed why did you agree to drive us here?'

'That was before I had spent an hour in the company of Nurse Ball.'

'Please, Charles. I simply want to see our Prime Minister in person, to make up my own mind. You've always encouraged that in me.'

He bows his head. The lines of age now etched deep into his forehead give him an exaggerated frown. 'I've made my views clear. You must do as you see fit.'

To ask for any more concessions might lose her the one she has already gained. Marie opens the door and hurries after Anne. No more than a few steps along the quay she's gagging at the stench. Fishing trawlers are moored alongside, unloading their catches. She is swept up by the crowds surging towards the ancient bridge that joins the two parts of the town, heading for the station at East-the-Water. For a moment she is glad of the crush protecting her from the full force of the wind sweeping down the river.

It's a different matter when she reaches the steps to the platform on the far side. It's a miracle she's not pitched over the wall onto the road below with all the pushing and shoving. The whole town seems to have turned out for a glimpse of Mr Asquith. Not that anyone knows what he actually looks like.

The Bideford Gazette featured him in their cartoon of the week - but not lampooning him. A thoroughly respectful piece about the Right Honorable Herbert Henry Asquith's brilliant career. It's of little use as an aid to identification though.

THE PRIZE-WINNER.

Anne proves the equal of the crowd and they are soon lodged in a good spot on the platform. But before long the sun is out and the crush begins to feel unbearable.

'You're looking pale,' Anne stares at Marie. 'Do you feel faint?'

'Yes, a little. I'll move back, get some air. You stay here.'

There's a shout from further up the platform. 'Smoke above the cutting. He's almost here.'

Anne pushes forward. 'I'm going to try and get closer.'

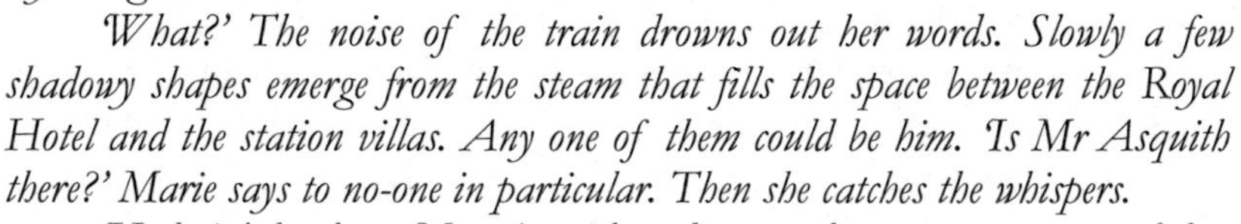

'What?' The noise of the train drowns out her words. Slowly a few shadowy shapes emerge from the steam that fills the space between the Royal Hotel and the station villas. Any one of them could be him. 'Is Mr Asquith there?' Marie says to no-one in particular. Then she catches the whispers.

'He bain't be there. Mrs Asquith and some other gentry sure enough but Asquith left the train at Exeter. Afraid of they suffragettes he is so he's coming up by car.'

The Mayor strains to make himself heard above the crowd and the bursts of steam from the engine. 'What's he saying?' Marie asks a woman beside her.

'Probably same thing he said last time.'

'Mr and Mrs Asquith have been to Bideford before?'

'Oh yes. Great friends with Mrs Hamlyn at Clovelly Court they are. Came for their honeymoon. That's when the Mayor stood here all preened up like a stuffed turkey waiting to launch into his welcoming address, but they'd come and gone before any of us knew what was happening. I just caught sight of them going over the bridge. Stopped all the traffic they did. Even cleared the road of horse droppings, couldn't offend the delicate nostrils of the gentry.

Looks like this time'll be no different.' She nods at the party already making their way down the steps to the waiting cars.

'Did you hear?' Anne appears beside Marie. 'Coward drove up from Exeter. Good to know we have him on the run though. We have to find Charles, get him to follow them to Clovelly.'

'He won't.'

'Why not? He brought us here. And it's not so much further.'

'You were very outspoken in the car. I haven't talked about our activities in such a direct way with him. He's… he's finding it challenging. We have to leave it for today.'

'But …'

'Please, Anne. I don't want this to cause a rift with my husband. He will support us, I know he will, but it will take time and patience.' Marie takes her arm. 'Let's go to Westward Ho! It's years since I've seen the beach there.'

The first editions of the local papers did their best to make a story out of the Prime Minister's non-appearance. According to them, Mr Asquith was obeying the irresistible call of the West, his soul fired by Charles Kingsley's descriptions of Clovelly's brawling streams, lichen-covered cottages, antique pier and wave-worn stones.

As it happens, Asquith was right to take evasive action, but a quick flight from the train was never going to deter the suffragettes. Travelling close behind were three women on a mission. Jessie Kenney, Vera Wentworth and Elsie Howey were young, fearless and determined to force an interview with Asquith.

Jessie, Annie Kenney's sister, had a flair for publicity stunts and a passionate commitment to the cause. Vera, a newer recruit, had mileage with Herbert Asquith. The previous year she'd been arrested for demonstrating outside his home and sentenced to three months, her third stint in Holloway. Elsie Howey was a well-to-do activist known for her powerful speaking voice and the set of steps she took everywhere to raise herself above the crowd.

In the spring of 1909, Annie Kenney hand-picked Vera and Elsie to spread the WSPU's message in South Devon. It wasn't a straightforward assignment; not because of any lack of interest in the cause, quite the opposite in fact. Prominent Plymouth families had supported women's suffrage since the 1860s and in 1873 an entirely male Plymouth Town Council voted to support a women's suffrage Bill before Parliament.

When Vera and Elsie arrived the real challenge was for supporters already affiliated to the NUWSS. Should they remain non-militant or join the new suffragettes? Mrs Pankhurst's speeches in Torquay and Plymouth left no-one in any doubt about the WSPU's militant stance and for a while they were not welcome. But they persevered. From rooms in an elegant stone house in Alfred Street on the Hoe, Plymouth, Vera organised monthly 'At Homes' at the Royal Hotel and meetings in the market place. Elsie focused on Torquay, even playing a barrel organ on the streets to publicise meetings at the Swiss Cafe and the Gerston Hotel in Paignton.

But when the papers announced that the Prime Minister would be spending Whitsun in Clovelly only one thought crossed their minds. Asquith had hidden behind a cordon of police as deputation after deputation of suffragettes tried for an audience with him at the House of Commons. But here there would be no cordon. It was too good an opportunity to miss. Even better, one of his guests at Clovelly Court was Lord Cromer, occasional President of the Men's League for Opposing Women's Suffrage. Two birds in the hand.

But how and when to confront them? A favourite tactic was to heckle government ministers at public meetings. But Asquith had refused an invitation from Barnstaple Liberal Association to be their guest, turning down any public engagements over his Whitsun holiday. The station was the next option but Asquith ducked out of any confrontation there by driving up from Exeter. That just left one, God-given, opportunity.

On Whit Sunday morning Mrs Hamlyn, their host at Clovelly Court, escorted Mr and Mrs Asquith through the grounds to church. It was Mrs Asquith who first spotted something unusual. All the

ladies in church were dressed in their Sunday best but none stood out more than the three young women in the pew opposite, dressed respectively in green, white and violet. Did Mrs Asquith realise the significance of the colours? Almost certainly; they were inescapable at suffragette demonstrations in London.

She handed her husband a note. It would be lovely to think it read 'Bandits at three o'clock,' but whatever it said, it ruffled Asquith, who kept casting furtive glances in the trio's direction. Doubtless he received broad smiles and nods of recognition in return. Asquith hurried out a side door as soon as the service was over but Jessie, Elsie and Vera caught up with him on the path and asked for a short interview. He was having none of it. 'Not a second,' he said and waved them away. The women were undaunted. Elsie and Vera, despite only being in their early twenties, were seasoned campaigners and had both served prison terms. A pompous, disgruntled politician wasn't going to intimidate them. 'Miss Woodlock is in prison while you are on your holiday,' they said. 'If you will not give us an

interview we will force one.' Miss Woodlock, a Liverpool suffragist, had been sentenced to Holloway a few months earlier.

Asquith was in no mood to listen and scuttled back to Clovelly Court. Jessie, Elsie and Vera regrouped at their accommodation in the village and occupied themselves in creative pursuits that were to come into their own less than twenty-four hours later.

The following morning they were back, playing a cat and mouse game - a phrase that came to hold a much more sinister meaning - with a police sergeant and a constable. Eventually they lost their pursuers by scrambling down the cliffs. They caught up with Asquith on the golf links and shouted their questions. 'Don't be a coward, Mr Asquith, receive the deputation on June 29,' and 'Why do you not release Patricia Woodlock?' But he refused to reply, ordering the police to remove them. A car was found and the three women were driven back to Bideford.

But the ladies weren't finished yet. They'd endured Holloway for nothing more than a peaceful protest. A Devon Bobby wasn't going to scare them off. They deposited their luggage at the station and set off on the eleven-mile hike back to Clovelly, a significant challenge in the dark. Arriving at the Court around two in the morning, they set to work on some horticultural decoration. Before long, bushes and shrubs across the gardens were covered in discs of paper proclaiming: 'Votes for Women,' 'Receive the deputation on June 29,' and 'Release Patricia Woodlock'. Copies of *Votes for Women* were strung as bunting along the balustrade and handkerchiefs decorated with paints borrowed from an artist in the village formed banners across the lawn. Even the sundial was draped with a decorated towel.

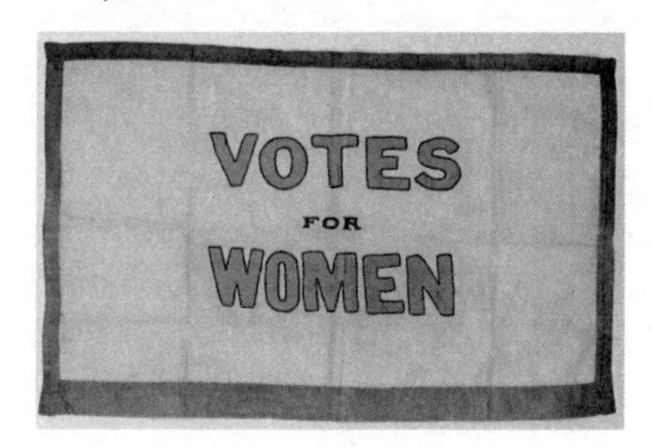

It must have been tempting to wait for Asquith to discover their handiwork. But it had been a long night and Jessie, Vera and Elsie still had the long walk back to Bideford, a round trip of twenty-two miles, before catching the early morning train to Exeter.

The local paper wasn't amused. According to the *Gazette* no-one would give political power to women capable of such tomfoolery. They pitied the mental state of anyone making themselves so obnoxious on the Sabbath. Perhaps it was naive to expect anything else. Even Mary Blathwayt, a steadfast supporter, called them hooligans. And, apart from Adela's visit a few months earlier, North Devon was virgin territory, full of respectable Liberal ladies never happier than chewing over a good scandal. How dare these women approach the Prime Minister? And when he was playing golf!

Curiously, the paper goes on to report: 'The last vestiges of the suffragettes' raid had barely been removed on Tuesday, when a lady dressed in black stopped at Clovelly Court and asked to see Mrs Hamlyn. She was asked from where she came, and replied ... 'Ilfracombe'. Having in mind that Miss Pankhurst is reported to be spending a holiday at Ilfracombe, the lady was asked her business. She replied that it had connection with the playing of the organ at Clovelly church, and gave her name as Miss Pond. Although the lady tried to obtain admission at the Court three times, she was unsuccessful.'

There are no more clues to the identity of the mystery woman. Perhaps Adela, having discovered the charms of Ilfracombe earlier that year? Or Sylvia? Christabel maybe? Or perhaps it was Marie Newby or Anne Ball, the fledgling WSPU supporters making their first foray into positive action.

Few in the South-West were ignorant of the suffragettes after that Whit weekend. One of the prime movers in the WSPU, Emmeline Pethick Lawrence, was speaking at Penzance the following week. The crowd took the chance to heckle her about the appalling behaviour of the women at Clovelly. She took the disapproval head on then gave as good as she got. It was time to remind these dyedin-the wool Cornishmen of one of their own protests that had passed into folklore - and song: 'And shall Trelawney live? Or shall Trelawney die? Here's twenty-thousand Cornish men, will know the reason why!' It went down well. 'If twenty-thousand Cornishmen wanted to know the reason why one of their countrymen was in prison,' Emmeline declared, 'why not three suffragists?'

A few weeks later Elsie and Vera made the headlines again. Earl Carrington, a Liberal MP, was due to address a meeting at the Victoria Hall in Exeter. It was another unmissable opportunity to heckle a government minister. The WSPU's publicity was spectacularly successful, attracting a crowd of over two thousand to hear them speak outside the hall. Vera challenged Earl Carrington as he arrived: 'Why will you not give votes to women?' No answer of course as he was escorted inside, but the crowd stayed to hear speeches from the women who more than once almost managed to force their way into the building. Even the local press praised their pluck and grit, saying it was a marvel of female endurance that they withstood the buffeting as they did.

Eventually Elsie and Vera, along with Mary Phillips, another WSPU organiser, were arrested. In court they thanked the people of Exeter, emphasising that their quarrel was not with the police but with the twenty men who formed the Cabinet who refused to give justice to women. The three women were sentenced to seven days' imprisonment.

Exeter prison might be a long way from Holloway but the treatment was no less harsh. The women's claim to be political prisoners was denied; they were sentenced as common criminals sharing the same conditions as convicted felons.

It wasn't simply the prison conditions that they railed against. Vera and Elsie made it clear at the outset that: 'having been placed in the third division, we felt it our duty to disobey the prison regulations and refuse food until placed in the first division ... We refused to go to our cells, but were forcibly removed there ... Presently we were told to come and put on prison dress. We refused, and were dressed by the warders and removed to fresh cells … Next day we were visited in turn by doctor, chaplain and governor, who all tried to persuade us to take food, the doctor threatening to feed us if necessary; and when we told him this was illegal he replied he would even certify us insane in order to do so!'

40 EXETER. — Devon County Prison. — LL.

Elsie, Vera and Mary became the first suffragette hunger strikers in the West Country. Mary Phillips wrote movingly of her experience:

> Never has a weapon been added to the armoury of women who fight for the Vote more powerful and sure than the hunger strike. It is also a shield against which the weapons of authority blunt and splinter themselves in vain… We told the governor at the beginning that we were going to disregard the rules and we told him why. Remonstrance was tried. Punishment was tried. Both were useless. Our duty was to "keep on" and we triumphed.
>
> When, on the third morning, I could not move from my bed or shout or sing any more to my fellow-prisoners, the doctor told me he would feed me by force. I thought, I cannot be responsible for what happens to my body; but I am responsible for my soul. I

> must "keep on". I said I am weak and cannot resist you. But I am determined. I will never yield voluntarily. I lay long in expectation of the doctor and his feeding apparatus but he did not come.

Mary Phillips was released after three days over concerns about her health. Elsie and Vera fasted for six days and although almost too weak to stand, kept their spirits up. After their release, they went to the Blathwayt's at Batheaston to recuperate. They were fed, watered, cared for and restored to health. They returned to South Devon as heroes, no longer simply Vera and Elsie but 'The Exeter Hunger Strikers'. Exeter WSPU organised a welcome home meeting and Torquay even presented Elsie with a clock. They may have abandoned the ladylike campaigning of the NUWSS but they were still most definitely Ladies!

Chapter Three
Lynton's Bow Street Connection
Summer 1909

While South Devon was building some momentum under Annie Kenney's leadership, North Devon was still relatively quiet. But in the summer of 1909, Ilfracombe had its first taste of a WSPU Summer Campaign. Ladies, with a capital 'L,' travelled from London intent on recruiting women through selling *Votes for Women* and speaking on the streets. These industrious visitors included Mari Pearce, staying at Rockcliffe on Capstone Parade and Miss Rind at Bloomfield Terrace. There was so much interest they easily sold out of magazines and urged speakers to come to the town to spread the word.

It was time for Annie to make her mark - just as soon as she'd recovered from events at a Liberal fete in Poole. She had planned to heckle the speaker, Winston Churchill, but before she'd said a word she was set upon: 'One man who was wearing the Liberal colours pulled a knife out of his pocket and ... started cutting my coat. He cut it in shreds right from the neck downwards. Then they lifted up my coat and started to cut my frock and cut my petticoat. A cry came from those Liberals, who are supposed to have high ideals in public life, to undress me. They took my hat and pulled down my hair ...'

Fortunately they had a change of heart and dragged her, bruised and battered, out of the grounds. It was this brutality, and worse, that suffragettes constantly experienced. But far from being deterred, Annie was fired with a renewed determination to spread the WSPU message in an intensive campaign across the South West.

She began in Dorset, a county where one person guaranteed to draw in the respectable ladies of the neighbourhood was the Honourable Evelina Haverfield, someone who was to play a significant role in North Devon. A typical aristocrat, Evelina Haverfield was an excellent horsewoman but distant, emotionally reserved, with a proud disdain for others - until she found her voice with the WSPU. Just a few months earlier, on June 29th, she and Mrs Pankhurst appeared in a headline-grabbing courtroom battle. The WSPU had discovered an 1869 Bill of Rights that stated: 'It is the right of the subject to petition the King and all commitments and prosecutions for such petitioning are illegal.' As the power of the King had passed to Parliament, their reasoning went, this clause now applied to Parliament's representative, the Prime Minister. Mrs Pankhurst and Mrs Haverfield challenged Asquith to accept a deputation with a petition. He refused. The 1869 ball was now firmly in their court.

News of the challenge spread and thousands lined the streets surrounding Parliament as Mrs Pankhurst, Evelina Haverfield and six others marched towards the House of Commons to the sound of the revolutionary Marseillaise played by the Women's Drum and Fife Band. Cheered by the crowds, they reached Parliament Square where an Inspector handed Mrs Pankhurst a letter. She read it aloud: 'The Prime Minister ... regrets that he is unable to receive the proposed deputation.' She threw it to the ground. 'I stand upon my right as a subject of the King to petition the Prime Minister. I am firmly resolved to stand here until I am received.'

The response was emphatic. She would not be allowed to enter.

To shortcut the usual violence for her frail companions, Mrs Pankhurst struck the Inspector, forcing an arrest of the eight. But it wasn't the end of the protest. Wave after wave of suffragettes, furious at the way the women had been treated, hurled stones covered with messages through government windows: 'Grant to the tax-paying women of Britain, the Vote'; 'Votes for Women this session'; 'Taxation without Representation is Tyranny'. By the end of the night, 107 women and eight men had been arrested.

The press was divided. *The Manchester Courier* was largely for the women: 'Principles and tact alike are wanting in the Asquith administration, otherwise there would have been none ... of the tumult and expense of last night ... No-one supposes for a moment that such a large and influential body as the suffragettes would have been denied a hearing by Mr Asquith and his colleagues had it possessed voting power ... '

Using more colourful language, *The Liverpool Daily Post and Mercury* was uncompromisingly against:

> The shrieking sisterhood have suffered another rebuff. The impudence and folly of the militant Suffragists are passing all bounds. There is no limit to the conceit of these misguided ladies. The unfortunate thing is that the cause of Woman Suffrage as represented by moderate and sensible women and men is being put back for years. It is being entirely destroyed by the methods of fanatic disorder of which yesterday's events in London were only one illustration. Reasonable people who

previously have supported the enfranchisement of women where the necessary qualifications exist, are made apathetic on the subject, and even driven into absolute antagonism by the irresponsible outbursts of these howling fanatics who are a public nuisance and must be suppressed.

'Shrieking sisterhood,' 'howling fanatics,' 'impudence and folly'! How could the WSPU get the nation to take them seriously with this kind of coverage? The answer - in that pillar of the British establishment, its courts. The time had come for one of the most significant legal challenges of the WSPU's campaign. The stage was set at Bow Street Magistrates Court where, in Sylvia Pankhurst's words: 'a sensation was created by the discovery that Lord Robert Cecil had been retained to defend the case of Mrs Haverfield upon which all the others hung.'

Evelina Haverfield (left) and Emmeline Pankhurst in the dock at Bow Street

Sitting on the bench was chief magistrate, Sir Albert de Rutzen. De Rutzen made a name for himself presiding over some high profile cases, including Oscar Wilde and Crippen, and was now an elder statesman of the court. Too elderly according to Sylvia Pankhurst who described him as: 'the old Magistrate with his half-shut eyes, who always reminded me of a tortoise.' But elderly or not, he was still the presiding magistrate and he made his view clear at the outset: 'It is a lamentable thing to see a respectable woman charged with the same sort of offence which is daily charged against small hooligan boys in the street. There can be no justification for women parading through the streets armed with stones and breaking public windows.'

The Bill of Rights defence was debated at length until De Rutzen, looking rather pained and blinking his eyes nervously, passed judgement: 'I agree with Lord Robert Cecil that the right of petition belongs to every subject but when the Prime Minister said he would not receive the deputation, the women acted wrongly in refusing to go away.' He imposed a fine of five pounds for resisting the police with the alternative of one month in the Second Division.

The women retaliated, claiming they were political offenders, not common criminals and should be put in the First Division. This would have given them certain privileges such as the right to wear their own clothes. De Rutzen refused, condemning them to the harshest conditions Holloway had to offer. It was one of a series of judgements against the suffragettes that was to have explosive significance as a chain of connections began to unravel connecting de Rutzen with the small Devon town of Lynton.

The twin towns of Lynton and Lynmouth sit on the coast where Exmoor meets the sea. The Victorians christened the area 'Little Switzerland,' capturing the drama and beauty of the steep, wooded river valleys that link the spectacular coastline with the expanse of the heather and bracken-covered moors. Many adopted the area for a home-grown grand tour when the Napoleonic wars made travel on the continent too risky. They arrived by train on the line from Barnstaple and moved between the two villages on the unique, water-powered cliff railway. Both were bequests from the town's most significant benefactor, Sir George Newnes. His generous gifts included the town hall, the Chapel and even the cricket pitch, a benign sward overlooked by the jagged profile of the Valley of the Rocks to the west of Lynton.

Sir George was introduced to the area by his friend and chess partner, Sir Thomas Hewitt, and by 1890 had bought land above the town known as Hollerday Hill. It's still a popular spot, with walkers taking the path up beside the town hall through the now crumbling gateposts by the lodge to follow the cutting Sir George had excavated to give the carriage horses an easier climb. A hairpin bend a little further on offers a spectacular view, at its best on a summer afternoon when the sun brings out the stunning colours on Countisbury Hill.

Pride of place at the very top of Hollerday Hill was given to the imposing three-storied mansion commissioned by Sir George. No expense was spared. Inside its stone and mullioned facade it offered twenty-one bedrooms, three bathrooms, several staircases, a clutch of reception rooms and a magnificent billiard room. The main room was vast, a good tennis court long and wide with the ceiling and walls panelled in oak. The oak continued through the floors and the substantial staircase. There was no stinting on the furnishings either. Persian rugs, Chippendale chairs, Japanese screens, old English sideboards, and mahogany writing desks inlaid with delicate marquetry. The walls overlooking all this opulence were covered with Sir George's collection of modern masters.

Outside was just as grand with a south-facing terrace, a croquet lawn, tennis court, bowling green and scented rose garden. Sir George generously shared much of his forty-acre estate with people from the twin towns of Lynton and Lynmouth. Hollerday House was also a magnet for some well-known figures of the day, often connections made through Sir George's publishing empire. His runaway successes were *Tit-Bits* and *The Strand Magazine*. In May 1901, *Tit-Bits* broke the news that: 'presently [Mr Conan Doyle] will give us an important story to appear in the Strand, in which the great Sherlock Holmes is the principal character.' A few weeks later *The Hound of the Baskervilles* made its debut. Arthur Conan Doyle became a personal friend and was guest of honour when the town unveiled the bust of Sir George at the new town hall.

Significantly, Conan Doyle and Sir George had politics in common. Sir George became a Liberal MP in 1885, initially for the constituency of Newmarket then Swansea from 1900, while Conan

Doyle stood as a Liberal Unionist in Edinburgh. One topic he was quite clear on was women's suffrage. In an address to the National League for Opposing Woman Suffrage, given soon after a particularly destructive spate of militancy, the Times reported: 'Mr Conan Doyle said it was necessary to differentiate between the honest Constitutional Suffragist, the female hooligans and the even more contemptible class of people who supplied the latter with money to carry out their malicious monkey tricks ... He believed that two years ago they might have had a chance of getting the vote but now they would not get it in a generation.'

Sir George was known for being a strong, rumbustious man, with a great presence, but throughout 1909 this began to change. The official line was that it was diabetes; village gossip had it as drink and depression. He'd go walkabout for days on end, no-one knew where, a symptom of a gradual breakdown that cost him a peerage. There was also talk of debts. Some said he was a gambler, others that he'd lost his touch and made bad investments. He sank thousands into an expedition to the Antarctic and even more into a disastrous mining concern in Australia. Whatever the reason, by the end of 1909, with his health failing, he decided to leave politics, standing down from his Swansea seat at the January election. His retirement was planned and anticipated. By contrast, the defeat of his son, Frank, also a Liberal MP, was a crushing blow, undermining Sir George's health even further.

A few months later he was dead. It was a time of mourning for the twin villages of Lynton and Lynmouth. Businesses were closed for the day and hundreds lined the route of the funeral procession for Sir George's final journey to the burial plot at the top of the town's graveyard, as close as he could get to his beloved Hollerday estate.

Shortly after his death the truth emerged. There was nothing left of the wealth he had so generously shared with Lynton over the years. Frank Newnes had already taken on much of his father's work, becoming President of George Newnes Ltd, but it was an uphill struggle saddled with enormous debts. Two years later he tried to sell the Hollerday estate.

By order of the Executors of the late Sir George Newnes, Bart
FINEST POSITION ON THE COAST
Magnificently positioned from 400 to 800 feet above sea
VERY BEAUTIFUL HOUSE
Commanding views of vast extent and surpassing grandeur
NORTH DEVON - "HOLLERDAY HOUSE", LYNTON, a superbly positioned and unique marine residence.

It failed to reach the reserve. The contents were auctioned but the house remained unsold. It was to remain empty for another two years, until one night in August 1913 when its political past caught up with it through the very prominent connections of Frank Newnes.

As the face of George Newnes Ltd, Frank Newnes was now the man responsible for the Liberal supporting *Westminster Gazette* founded by his father, a very public association with Liberal policy and politics. More significantly for the events that were to unfold, Frank Newnes was married to Emmeline August Louisa, daughter of Albert Richard Francis Maximilien de Rutzen. The same Sir Albert de Rutzen who was the Chief Magistrate at Bow Street Court; the man responsible for dismissing Mrs Pankhurst and Evelina Haverfield's legal challenge and for sentencing hundreds of suffragettes to the degradation of the Second Division at Holloway.

THE ILLUSTRATED
LONDON NEWS,

REGISTERED AT THE GENERAL POST OFFICE AS A NEWSPAPER.

No. 3634. — VOL. CXXXIII. SATURDAY, DECEMBER 12, 1908. SIXPENCE.

THE WOMAN WITH THE WHIP: THE MILITANT SUFFRAGETTES' NEW WEAPON IN USE AT THE ALBERT HALL.

DRAWN BY OUR SPECIAL ARTIST, S. BEGG.

Chapter Four
The Woman with the Whip
Autumn 1909

Throughout 1909, Annie Kenney worked tirelessly to extend the reach of the WSPU across the West Country. After Dorset, she and Evelina moved on to Somerset, holding meetings in Wellington and Street, then Bampton in Devon. Annie was a powerful speaker but she was constantly heckled on the WSPU's militancy; particularly when one tactic spawned a hostile headline in the *Pall Mall Gazette: An Outrage Unparalleled in English History*. A suffragette attacked a polling station at the Bermondsey by-election, breaking bottles of corrosive acid over ballot boxes to destroy the contents and blinding the presiding officer in one eye. It was bad enough that suffragettes vandalised post boxes and smashed windows but it was beyond the pale for an innocent bystander to suffer.

The truth was rather different. Yes, Alice Chapin had broken a test tube over a ballot box and the liquid, emphatically *not* corrosive acid, did splash the presiding officer, but even he said it was an accident and far from being blinded there was a possibility of a slight haze to his sight. But the *Pall Mall Gazette* reflected the tone of the press. Militancy was in danger of backfiring as the WSPU increasingly lost the battle against press bias - a bias that played to the fears of many.

Soon after Bermondsey, a Mr Hopper from Barnstaple spoke to Braunton Women's Liberal Association. He was ardently pro-suffrage. Women had proved themselves capable leaders in other walks of life, he said, and always came down on the side of right with constructive laws. It was absurd to keep them out of politics. But, and on this he was unequivocal, no self-respecting Government would give the vote to militants after Bermondsey.

Even some WSPU core supporters were having second thoughts. After getting so close to Asquith at Clovelly, Elsie and Vera tried again when he visited the Kent village of Lympne. But this time Vera, not content with a verbal assault, actually lashed out at Asquith. For a woman to speak disrespectfully to her elders and betters was bad enough, but to physically assault the Prime Minister! It was an action that sent shock waves through middle England. Emily Blathwayt, previously one of the suffragettes greatest supporters, wrote: 'We hear of terrible things by the two hooligans, Vera and Elsie ... Vera was the violent one.'

Vera was unrepentant: 'We are driven nearly mad by the unjust treatment all our dear women have received. I am sorry you are grieved but if Mr Asquith will not receive our deputation we will pummel him again.'

It was too much for Emily Blathwayt. The following morning she wrote to the secretary of the WSPU: 'Dear Madam, with great reluctance I am writing to ask that my name may be taken off the list as a Member of the WSPU Society. When I signed the membership paper, I thoroughly approved of the methods then used. Since then, there has been personal violence and stone throwing which might injure innocent people ... people of my village who have hitherto been full of admiration for the Suffragettes are now feeling very differently.' Although she continued to offer respite at her home near Bath for suffragettes released from prison, she became increasingly anxious about their militant tactics. If stones didn't work would the WSPU resort to bombs?

Vera quoted the appalling brutality being used towards women by Liberal stewards to justify her actions, a view shared by another suffragette in the headlines. In December 1908, David Lloyd George, the then Chancellor, was booked to speak at the Albert Hall. Emmeline Pankhurst warned that the WSPU would heckle if he didn't pledge government action. Of course, there was no pledge, so as soon as he started speaking, women sprang up chanting, 'We want deeds, not words!' Two rows were dressed in prison uniform, a protest at the three hundred suffragettes who had been imprisoned for the cause. It was another example of the brilliant tactics employed by the WSPU, many of them stemming from the creative genius of Sylvia Pankhurst. Like Vera, Elsie and Jessie's decision to wear the colours at Clovelly, this demonstration created a visual impact guaranteed to hit the headlines - although overshadowed on this occasion by subsequent events.

Helen Ogston was a science graduate and frequent speaker with the WSPU. In her second tier box above the action, she watched and waited, intent on picking the perfect moment. The stewards were treating the women with their usual brutality. It was something they had come to expect. It was why she had hesitated by her closet, then reached inside for something she concealed beneath her coat before setting off for the meeting. As order was restored she leapt to her feet crying 'Votes for Women'. Immediately the stewards scaled the rows towards her, intent on hauling her away. One even pressed a lighted cigar against her wrist. She reacted immediately, pulling a dog whip from beneath her cloak and flicking it towards the men. There was never any intent to harm but it was manna from heaven for papers around the world.

> *Suffragettes Riot in Albert Hall*
> (The New York Times)
> *Militant Suffragettes New Weapon in Use at the Albert Hall*
> (Illustrated London News)

They were headlines to challenge even the most ardent supporter. Could using a weapon ever be justified? Especially one that had been selected, concealed and carried to the event in the cold light of day. Helen Ogston wrote to *Votes for Women* to explain her actions:

Why I Used the Dog Whip

> Sir - It has been stated freely in the Press that I used a dog-whip on Saturday last to prevent my eviction from Mr Lloyd George's meeting. This statement is entirely incorrect. I used a dog-whip not to prevent eviction, but as a protest against violent assault.
>
> On one or two previous occasions when I have been present to heckle Cabinet Ministers I have been subjected to very serious violence, and both I and other women have been disgracefully mauled by the stewards. I determined, accordingly, on Saturday, to take steps to prevent a recurrence of such treatment, and to make a protest against it. I therefore took a dog-whip with me.
>
> When I made my interruption, I was at once set up on by the stewards, and knocked backwards by a man who was sitting in the next box. I informed them that I was prepared to leave the building, but I refused to submit to their handling. This statement was absolutely disregarded, and I was dealt with - with great

violence; in the course of the melée I struck with my whip at one of the men who was behaving brutally.

In common with other members of the Women's Social and Political Union, I have the strongest natural repugnance to violence - but I felt it my duty in this instance to make a protest against the sort of treatment to which no woman ought to submit.

Yours Etc., Helen Ogston.

In early December 1909, Marie Newby, Anne Ball and other supporters from Ilfracombe had the chance to make up their own minds. Annie Kenney arranged for Helen Ogston to speak in Barnstaple. The churchyard surrounding the parish rooms was overflowing with locals ready to heckle 'the woman with the whip'. If they were expecting an Amazon they would have been disappointed. Helen Ogston was a mild-mannered, gently spoken lady. Inside the parish rooms, she set out to persuade her audience that the suffrage campaign wasn't a war between men and women. Convincing her audience that militancy was justified was a challenge after the events at Bermondsey and her own actions at the Albert Hall, but, she asked, what else could they do? They had tried peaceful, polite campaigning for over half a century and still politicians refused to listen to them. Surely they couldn't be blamed if they'd become a bit disorderly!

There was a falling-out in the hall over the suffragette's blanket policy of opposing all Liberals at by-elections but Miss Ogston was convincing. It was, she said, the only way they could force the Liberal Government to live up to its own principles - that taxation and representation should go hand-in-hand, and that the will of the majority should prevail: the majority, that is, of MPs in the House of Commons and Asquith's own Cabinet, majorities he stubbornly and persistently refused to act on. It was a flagrant abuse of democracy and an unbelievable act of arrogance by a man intent on flouting the will of Parliament. But Asquith had met his match. In the suffragettes, the immovable object had met the unstoppable force.

Asquith's personal opposition to women's suffrage was well known. He'd publicly stated that he thought it bad for women and bad for the country. He'd shown his true colours the previous year when he offered to abandon his resistance if it could be demonstrated that enough women wanted the vote. It was a clever tactic on his part. What was enough? How did it need to be demonstrated?

With their usual military efficiency, in June 1908 the women responded with the biggest procession London had ever seen. Suffrage groups, professionals, academics, churches and more from all over the country converged on the capital, creating a procession that took over two hours to pass spectators lining the route.

GREAT VOTES FOR WOMEN DEMONSTRATION IN HYDE PARK, SUNDAY. JUNE 21. 1908.

A crowd of 250,000, some papers estimated anything up to 500,000, poured into Hyde Park to hear speakers from all the Suffrage organisations, an event proclaimed by *Votes for Women* as *'The Largest Political Demonstration in the History of the World.'*

Yet Asquith still refused to introduce a Bill on women's suffrage.

Christabel Pankhurst, now chief organiser of the WSPU, was incensed. 'Women are being defrauded, insulted, and dishonoured,' she said. 'It is time to demand a Bill giving women taxpayers the parliamentary right of representation. Why should women pay taxes if they have no say in how they are spent?'

There may have been widespread sympathy with the message but the means were still very much up for debate. In December, Kate James, who had spoken at the YMCA debate earlier that year, made her stand at a meeting at the Albert Hall - Barnstaple's Albert Hall that is, the building that stood on the site of the present Queen's Theatre. 'Speaking as a Suffragist,' she said, 'I strongly dissociate myself from the methods being adopted by militant suffragettes.' A mild rebuff compared to the opposition Evelina Haverfield experienced when presiding at a meeting in Yeovil. She endured catcalls, booing, rattles, raucous singing, laughter, fireworks and missiles - coal, apples, bundles of wet paper and worse. In the chaos that ensued, chairs were broken and those on the platform had to beat back the hooligans with sticks. Evelina adamantly refused to close the meeting but the police eventually intervened, clearing the platform and escorting the suffragettes back to their lodgings.

Undaunted, the WSPU pressed on. In January 1910, Asquith called a General Election. There is no record of whether Marie, Anne and others lobbied against Sir Ernest Soares in North Devon but it would have been a significant challenge. Sir Ernest Soares, a flamboyant Portuguese East-Indian solicitor from Manchester, had been the Liberal MP for Barnstaple for ten years. He was an unlikely figure to represent this Devon outpost but local people took to him, returning him with a majority of over two thousand at the previous election. It would have taken a massive swing to unseat him.

Annie Kenney decided to focus on West Country seats where Liberal candidates had a much slimmer majority. In Exeter, Harold St Maur had scraped in with just eighty-five votes last time around. Mrs Pankhurst had overturned a majority of more than a thousand in Mid Devon. How hard could eighty-five be?

The women went into overdrive producing posters, pamphlets, leaflets, postcards, badges - none of it pulling any punches. *The Right Dishonourable Double-Face Asquith* was available in three sizes for hoardings, palings and windows.

It was a campaign run with military efficiency; women across the country were briefed on why the WSPU was anti-Asquith, the appalling treatment of suffragettes in prison and why it was so important to fight for the vote. After years of relentless campaigning, suddenly a few weeks of all-out effort could bring them victory. Toppling one Liberal MP wouldn't get them the vote but it was a start. Their message was clear.

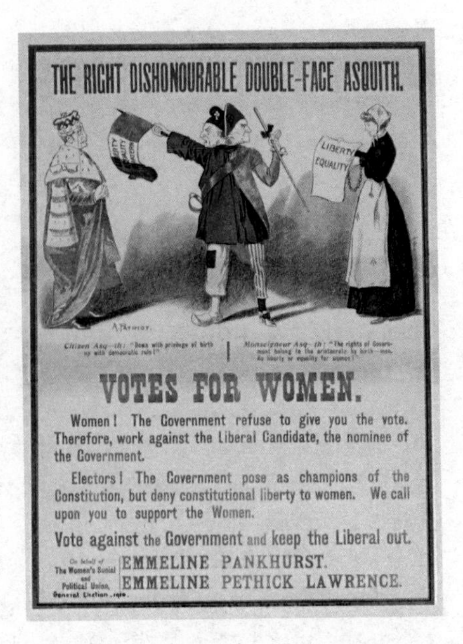

EVERY VOTE AGAINST THE GOVERNMENT IS A VOTE FOR HUMAN LIBERTY AND JUSTICE TO WOMEN

EVERY VOTE FOR A LIBERAL CANDIDATE IS A VOTE FOR FORCE FEEDING AND THE ILL-TREATMENT OF WOMEN POLITICAL PRISONERS

VOTE FOR THE WOMEN AND KEEP THE LIBERAL OUT

The Exeter branch of the WSPU leapt into electioneering action. They were spurred on by reports that Asquith was so afraid of being accosted by suffragettes that his police guard smuggled him into a Bristol meeting through a vegetable patch, then out through the gooseberry bushes. The glory of it was, there were no suffragettes! They were all busy campaigning on the other side of the city, but the image of their double-dealing Prime Minister cowering amongst the cabbages created better publicity than any encounter could have done.

The campaign in Exeter was organised from committee rooms at 16 Longbrook St, a double-fronted corner shop overflowing with Sylvia Pankhurst's stunning election posters, leaflets, badges and banners. The women's schedule was exhausting with four open-air meetings held daily on sites across town: Paris Street, the tram terminus, Sidwell Street, the Iron Bridge, New North Road, Larkbear, Fore Street, Heavitree Road, Queen Street ... all the same pitches used by the election candidates.

Gladice Keevil was drafted in from WSPU headquarters as organiser - a flamboyant character known for her rousing speeches and panache with hecklers. She was described by *The Daily News* as: '... a particularly striking figure. Robed in flowing white muslin, her lithe figure swayed to every changing expression, and the animated face that smiled and scolded by turns beneath the black straw hat and waving white ostrich feather, was the centre of one of the densest crowds.'

In the second week of January 1910, Gladice Keevil took time out to support Marie Newby and Anne Ball in Ilfracombe. They were joined by Helen Ogston, without her whip this time, who stayed for an 'At Home' in Barnstaple parish rooms the following afternoon. She was on good form, so fluent on militant tactics that even the local paper described her as a delightful speaker. Meanwhile, Gladice moved on to Torquay where she used a decorated cart to travel the entire constituency on polling day, campaigning to the end.

Annie Kenney drew unprecedented crowds in Bridgwater - as many as ten thousand according to *Votes for Women*. The

Conservative won the seat with a majority of over 1,500. Even the sceptics conceded it was down to the suffragettes.

Exeter were also jubilant after ousting the Liberal. It was tight, the Conservative only had a majority of twenty-six, but the women had done it. In seven constituencies across the West Country they proved they could unseat Liberal candidates. Asquith had to listen now, particularly given his precarious position. He'd scraped back into power with a majority dependent on the whims of the Irish Nationalists.

But it was another story in Torquay. Workers from the local WSPU had been on a knife-edge during the count. Then the agonising result. They had whittled down the Liberal majority by over 700, but the candidate had held on by a handful of votes. With a different result here and in a few more constituencies across the country they might even have toppled Asquith's government.

The WSPU may not have been completely victorious but they had certainly shaken things up. Immediately after the election, MPs formed a committee to draft a Private Member's Suffrage Bill. The WSPU had heard it all before, so many Bills, none making it through Parliament, but this time there were two significant differences. All the parties were involved and the chair was Lord Lytton, brother of Lady Constance Lytton, a committed suffragette who had herself been imprisoned in Holloway. Imagine Christabel Pankhurst's delight. If anything vindicated her policy of recruiting ladies with influence this was it.

It was a pivotal moment. Everyone held their breath as the two militant organisations, the WSPU, led by the Pankhursts, and the Women's Freedom League, led by Charlotte Despard, discussed a temporary suspension of militancy. To the relief of many, they announced there would be no confrontations while such a positive initiative was in the offing.

Keen to take advantage of the political truce, the committee of MPs issued a letter for publication nationwide, including in the *Ilfracombe Chronicle:* 'Soon after the House of Commons meets, a Bill will be introduced under the ten minutes' rule, as a private member's measure ... The effect will be to enfranchise about a million new electors ... a cautious advance which respects the preference of Unionists for a moderate and experimental solution ... The committee has no doubt that the Bill could be passed by a large majority. Its fate depends on the readiness of the Government to grant the two or three days necessary for its consideration.'

'Its fate depends on the readiness of the Government to grant the two or three days necessary for its consideration.' Years of struggle came down to this one decision - that rested with Asquith.

The WSPU were determined to keep the pressure on. They organised more meetings, more rallies, more sales of *Votes for Women* than ever before. The highlight was to be the most spectacular demonstration yet of public support for the cause - a Great March. But an event no-one anticipated intervened. With heavy black-lined columns, on May 6th 1910, the *Ilfracombe Chronicle* announced: 'His Majesty the King breathed his last at 11.45 tonight; in the presence of Her Majesty the Queen Alexandra, the Prince and Princess of Wales, the Princess Royal and the Duke of Fife, the Princess Victoria and the Princess Louise. Though prepared for the worst by the series of grave bulletins issued during the previous two days, the profound sorrow with which the nation heard that the fears for its beloved Sovereign's life were so unhappily well-founded was made more poignant by the brevity of his illness.'

Chapter Five

The Man is Not for Turning

Spring 1910

After the sombre news of the death of the King the women were lifted by more positive news from Parliament. The first stage of the Private Member's Suffrage Bill had passed through the House of Commons. Not only passed but with a massive majority. The tide was turning!

The Great March was reorganised for June 18th. They would show Asquith once and for all that women must have the vote. *Votes for Women* announced: 'The vast army of women which will march through the streets on that day will do more than express an academic belief in the vote; it will be definitely calling upon Mr Asquith to secure the passage of the Woman Suffrage Bill through Parliament ... this session. As it winds its way along ... it will be marching not merely to its objective - the Albert Hall - but also to the dawn of a broader and better day for women.'

Emmeline Pethick-Lawrence, co-founder of the WSPU with Emmeline Pankhurst, urged readers to ask what the march would mean:

> To those who have grown white in the fifty-year struggle for emancipation: this great muster of women, unprecedented in the world's history is the reward of their labour and their faith, and this is to them a crowning day.
>
> To prisoners: It means that the song of victory which they sang in the silence of the prison cell has been taken up by thousands of hearts and is sung to-day to the rhythm of marching feet.
>
> To the rank and file: To that great army drawn from all the Suffrage Societies, from all the professions, from all the classes, from the study, the factory and the home, it means the promise of a better future, the hope of a surer foothold in life from which to stretch out helping hands to the hopeless, the helpless and the weak.

For the first time, Devon women would be marching shoulder-to-shoulder with their sisters in London. An excursion was organised from Exeter with a special train to get participants to the embankment by 5.30, returning in the early hours of the next morning. The organisation was impeccable with everyone marshalled into groups, the West of England ladies lining up along the embankment in section B3. Thousands of women waited for their cue to step out towards the Royal Albert Hall, significantly with the Honourable Evelina Haverfield and Vera Holme, someone else who was to become familiar in Devon, riding up and down the lines like marshals seeing to the arrangement of their forces.

A women's drum and pipe band - one of thirty - followed, heralding 617 women all dressed in white, a dramatic representation of the number of prison sentences handed out by Asquith's government.

Groups from all over the country streamed behind them through the capital: women graduates, university men, suffragettes displaying the yellow, white and green of the Women's Freedom League, nurses, business women, teachers, artists, writers, civil servants, clerks, typists and more. It was a demonstration every bit as impressive as the one held almost exactly a year earlier. The question was, how would Asquith react?

A week later they had their answer. 'The Government cannot afford any further facilities [time] for the Bill this session.' There was uproar with 189 MPs signing a petition demanding Asquith find time to pass the Bill. Even the press didn't hold back:

> Men were deceivers ever. *Nottingham Guardian*.
> Mr Asquith has been the drag on the whole of the Suffragist movement. He is convinced of the undesirability of conceding the Parliamentary Franchise to women. That being so, he has found it easy to plead all sorts of difficulties as excuses for not handling the subject. *Aberdeen Free Press*.
> Once more the Prime Minister's tactics are exposed as mere subterfuge. *Morning Advertiser*.
> Suffragist pioneers ... must be getting a little tired of "jam tomorrow, but never jam to-day"; the promised land is always in sight, but it always eludes the weary marchers. *The Globe*.
> I may say frankly that their [the militants] ranks will be reinforced daily by non-militants and by members of the Women's Liberal Federation, of whom many have begun to despair of peaceful methods. *Western Daily Mercury*.

Magically, Asquith suddenly found two free days in the middle of July for the second reading. The women were back in the game. It was tight, but there was just enough time for a two-day debate on the second reading, a week in Committee, back to the House for the report stage and the third reading then up to the House of Lords before Parliament rose for the summer - provided there was no more obstruction from the Government. Even the most hardened optimist had to face that possibility.

At the second reading, the Bill passed with a majority of 109, an emphatic 'Yes!' to Votes for Women - no ifs, no buts, no maybes ... Apart from in the mind of one man. Just before the summer recess, Asquith was at it again, announcing there would be no further time for the later stages of the Bill. He was determined to stop women getting the vote, his views as entrenched as in his first major speech on women's suffrage delivered almost two decades earlier: 'The vast majority of women do not want the vote. Women are not fit for the franchise. Women operate by personal influence. And perhaps most significantly, it would upset the natural order of things. Women's place is in the home rather that in the "dust and turmoil" of political life.' Heaven forbid that the voices of hundreds of thousands of women should overturn his home comforts!

Asquith's cover was well and truly blown. Moderates from the Women's Liberal Association resigned in droves. The Men's Suffrage League recommended an anti-government policy. Even the press conceded a return to militancy would be justified. The Suffrage Bill, that had come closer to passing into law than any before it, was on a knife-edge.

With the WSPU poised on the brink of a return to violence, Keir Hardie, former leader of the Labour party, suggested a way forward. He would press for a third reading as soon as Parliament reopened in the autumn. The logic was overwhelming. Asquith had played his hand cleverly, making his announcement on the cusp of the summer recess. Nothing could be done until Parliament reconvened in three months. The suffragettes agreed to wait, but that didn't mean they would be idle. The Women's Freedom League issued a rallying call: 'We must go on fighting until, in the face of prejudice and intolerance, we have won our liberties. On the day Parliament closed, the new campaign opened, and from now on, everyone who desires the enfranchisement of women must work unceasingly to rouse the country ... the campaign must grow in force and effectiveness until by November we have raised a protest which cannot easily be overlooked or disregarded.'

Ilfracombe responded to the call. Marie Newby and Anne Ball gathered a growing band of supporters around them, enthusiastically embracing the WSPU's call to action with an active holiday campaign. They set their inhibitions aside and took to the streets to demand 'Votes for Women', a step that took enormous courage. Respectable women protesting in the streets! Unthinkable! They would have found themselves shunned by friends and neighbours for whom this degrading activity was a step too far. In London the degradation went even further as women were forced to walk in the gutter to avoid being arrested for obstruction.

The campaign in North Devon was boosted by the arrival of Helen Craggs, an organiser from the WSPU's London headquarters. Significantly, two years later Helen was discovered at the country house of a well-known government anti-suffragist in possession of two cans of inflammable oil, two boxes of matches, four tapers, nine 'pick-locks', twelve fire-lighters, a hammer, an electric torch, and a piece of American cloth smeared with some sticky substance. She was charged with attempted arson, becoming the first suffragette imprisoned for plotting to damage property. Perhaps she shared her thoughts on militancy with Marie Newby during those sunny, summer weeks, thoughts that were to have explosive significance before too long.

Two other ladies, Mrs Mackworth and Miss Pridders, also stopped off for some campaigning in North Devon as part of a summer tour of the West Country. They settled into the Imperial in Barnstaple before making their mark, literally, on the town's streets. They introduced the locals to a practice familiar in the capital but a novelty in this rural market town - chalking the pavements. The North Devon Journal was intrigued: 'Last week, meetings in support of the Women's Suffrage movement were held on Thursday, Friday and Saturday evenings in the Strand, Barnstaple. The organisers announced the meeting by writing notices in chalk on pavements in leading thoroughfares, "Votes for Women" prefacing the announcements. The young lady who did the chalking in High St about midday on Thursday naturally attracted a good deal of attention. She met with some protests and in several cases the notices were promptly obliterated. There was a fair attendance at the opening meeting and the speakers were afforded a good hearing. Much amusement was caused by the exhibition at the meeting of a notice some wags had prepared. It read, "Blokes for Women". A diverting parody of the familiar war cry of the Suffragettes.'

The summer of 1910 also saw a new arrival in Ilfracombe, Cerisa Palmer from County Wicklow, Ireland. She took up lodgings with Mrs Rowe in Avenue Road and almost immediately became a talking point in the town. Local residents mocked her odd appearance in a walking skirt and boots, covered by a long coat if it was wet, and her peculiar swimming costume. Despite her slender appearance she was a strong, if eccentric, swimmer. No matter what the weather, she bathed every day from the Tunnels beach.

Marie and her companions came to know Cerisa Palmer as well as anyone in Ilfracombe. She could appear stand-offish, formidable even, but at the flick of a switch a magnetic personality emerged. She was multi-talented, fluent in French, German, Italian and Russian, a gifted painter, and passionate about women's rights. That was when they caught a glimpse of the real Cerisa Palmer, someone who, they later discovered, was unstoppable when speaking on a subject close to her heart. There were hints of a book but attempts to discover more were met with silence - until the truth about Miss Cerisa Palmer finally emerged the following year, cloaked in tragedy.

At the beginning of September 1910, Annie Kenney was busy throughout the South West, drawing crowds at Axminster, Seaton, Lyme Regis and Sidmouth before finally arriving in Ilfracombe. Anticipation in the town was high, with hundreds buying their tickets for the Runnacleave Hall from Moore's in the High Street, available for a shilling or sixpence reserved, three pence unreserved. *Votes for Women* reported: 'Many new members were made and a local union is being formed at Ilfracombe in the course of a week or two.' A whirlwind had hit Ilfracombe and before they knew it Marie, Anne and other supporters were committed to turning their get-togethers into a formal WSPU group. Just a few weeks later, Annie was back to speak at their inaugural meeting, once again reported in *Votes for Women:*

> Ilfracombe and Barnstaple – FIRST REPORT. Mrs Newby kindly lent her drawing room on Thursday last to give Miss Kenney the opportunity of meeting Ilfracombe and Barnstaple members. A good number turned up and the new branch promises to be most active. It was decided to hold a meeting on Saturday, November 12th when Lady Isabel Margesson will speak. Miss Ball wishes all members and sympathisers to call for literature. All the new pamphlets are on sale, also VFW. Any person wanting information should write to Mrs Newby.

As well as Marie, now the Hon. Secretary and Treasurer, and Anne, the Literary Secretary, others who rallied to the call were Margaret Eldridge, Nurse Simes, Mrs Bennett, Mrs Page, Mrs Williams, Miss Ward, Miss Bendle, Miss Warren and Miss Wise. Flyers were distributed, envelopes addressed, and preparations made for the group's first big event. It was a tight schedule for Lady Isabel Margesson; she was booked at the Victoria Hall in Exeter the evening before, but everything was in place by the time the stewards ushered the audience into their seats at the Gaiety Hall.

The *Ilfracombe Gazette* was light on the detail of the speech but impressed by Lady Isobel's credentials: 'In the afternoon the elite of Ilfracombe and District assembled in that comfortable little hall to listen to an address by Lady Isabel Margesson on the subject of Women's Suffrage. Whatever might be one's views on this question, there cannot possibly be two opinions on the ability of Lady Margesson as an exponent of the principles she espouses... Lady Isobel is the daughter of the late Lord Hobart, whose father was the late Earl of Buckinghamshire.'

The *North Devon Journal* stepped into the breach, offering more coverage on her 'excellent address' to the people of Ilfracombe: '[Lady Isabel Margesson] presented the case with eloquence and moderation, and urged that as two-thirds of the legislation passed was domestic, women should at least have some voice in it. They had grievances as men had, and should have votes to try and get the grievances remedied. Much was done for the working man but little for the working woman, whose lot was hardly better than it was 50 years ago.' She ended with an appeal to her audience. 'Every Suffragist Society agrees with this [Conciliation Bill] and I hope you will do your utmost for the movement.'

She spoke again in the evening. Bishop Powell, in the chair, was adamant that the arguments against Woman Suffrage were far too feeble to obstruct the reform demanded by the women: 'Lady Isabel Margesson then gave another earnest and admirable address showing how the welfare of the country, in the opinion of the advocates of Woman Suffrage would be greatly advanced by the granting of the vote to women.'

During questions there was the inevitable challenge to militancy. But Lady Margesson was more than equal to the heckling, arguing that while anything done by the women was magnified by press and politicians, the rough and harsh treatment of their opponents was often suppressed. Applause greeted her plea for those present not to misjudge the women, but to focus on their work on behalf of those who could not help themselves. It was an effective rallying cry that prompted a rush of new members to the group. Demand was so great, they sold out of copies of *Votes for Women*.

Spirits were high. They might be remote from London, but ignited by Annie, the fight for the vote was alive and well in North Devon. Marie, Anne, Margaret and others in Ilfracombe would do whatever it took to achieve their aim. They were almost there. 'The Bill This Session' they declared. They didn't have long to wait. The Prime Minister's response to Keir Hardie's demand for a third reading was imminent. Just one last push.

The omens were not good. Asquith knew the women expected him to make time for the passage of the Bill, so why didn't he recall Parliament sooner for the autumn session? Why did he allow the House to rise early night after night? Why did he not extend the session? All very reasonable questions that left the women dreading yet another betrayal.

And there had been several.

June 1906: Asquith announced his intention, before the close of Parliament, to bring in an electoral reform bill to which a woman suffrage amendment could be moved. Parliament ended without this pledge being honoured.

December 1909: Asquith promised that his pledge would hold good for the Parliament of 1910 and that plenty of time would be given to deal with the whole question. Parliament ended without this pledge being honoured.

June 1910: Having announced there was no time for a Suffrage Bill, Asquith buckled under pressure and conceded a second reading, but then dug his heels in, refusing any further time for the later stages of the Bill.

Suffragettes clung to their demand, insisting that Parliament earn women's support and enter the Bill on the Statute Book that year. But a call to arms was not far behind. An article in the Women's Freedom League's mouthpiece, *The Vote,* made it plain: 'In spite of the obstacles still to be overcome, we believe that the Conciliation Bill can be carried into law during the autumn. But while we are prepared for victory and struggling to it, common prudence dictates that we must hold ourselves ready to meet any and every emergency. We must be prepared for such happenings as will commit us inevitably to a second recourse to militancy – the weapon of the rebel.

'The rejection of this Bill will entail greater expenditure of effort and more deliberate intention to destroy and more flagrant violation of the wishes of the House of Commons. It will be an insult and an injury beyond that implied in past rejections. It will reveal a more determined immorality in the Governmental opponent. It will be the throwing down of a gauge of battle. It will commit us inevitably to further militant action. We cannot repeat, we must progress. We shall find ourselves committed to action upon more drastic lines, to action having more serious effects, to sterner and stronger measures. This will be inevitable.'

Asquith's announcement was expected on Friday, November 18th. Women gathered en masse at Caxton Hall to wait. If this was to be yet another betrayal they would march on Parliament, spurred on by a missive from Christabel Pankhurst a few days earlier: 'The deputation of women which proceeds to Westminster on Friday must be taken as a sign that women are now determined not any longer to beg for justice but to take it … a new chapter opens in the history of the active movement for the enfranchisement of women. We know perfectly well they will never do anything for us unless we drive them into doing it. This truce has taught us a great deal. It has taught us the absolute necessity for militancy. It is no good sitting at home and talking: it is no good simply wishing for success; we must give some outward manifestation of the feeling that we have in our hearts. We hope that every woman will consider whether it is not right and suitable for her to send in her name, whether it is not her sheer and absolute duty.'

Hundreds responded to her call to action, filling Caxton Hall at noon to wait. Then came the news. There would be no time for the final stages of the Conciliation Bill. No more self-delusion. Asquith had done what Mrs Pankhurst and Christabel suspected he would all along. After every suffragist and suffragette in the country had placed their trust in him, he had betrayed them. Again. The truce was over.

Over 300 women left the hall in detachments of twelve, the first led by Mrs Pankhurst and Evelina Haverfield. Very soon the defenceless women were being buffeted by plainclothes police brought in from outlying districts. The usual officers had become too sympathetic to the cause, so half-trained recruits from the East End had been drafted in. Sympathisers attempted to help, forcing a passage for Mrs Pankhurst towards Parliament Square. Cheers rang out when she was spotted on the steps to the Strangers Entrance and each time she was joined by others waving standards above the crowd declaring 'Where there's a Bill there's a Way,' and 'Women's Will beats Asquith's Won't.'

MISS SYLVIA PANKHURST

Within minutes the standards were torn down as police moved in on horseback. Sylvia Pankhurst forced herself to witness the brutality: 'I saw Miss Ada Wright rush the entrance. Several police seized her, lifted her from the ground and flung her back into the crowd. A moment afterwards she appeared again and I saw her running as fast as she could towards the House of Commons. A Policemen struck her with all his force and she fell to the ground. For a moment there was a group of struggling men round the place where she lay, then she rose up only to be flung down again immediately. Then a tall, grey-headed man with a silk hat was seen fighting to protect her, but three or four police seized hold of him and bundled him away.

'Then again I saw Miss Ada Wright's tall, grey-clad figure, but over and over again she was flung to the ground, how often I cannot say. It was a painful and degrading sight. At last she was lying against the wall of the House of Lords, close to the Strangers' Entrance and a number of women, with pale and distressed faces, were kneeling down round her. She was in a state of collapse.'

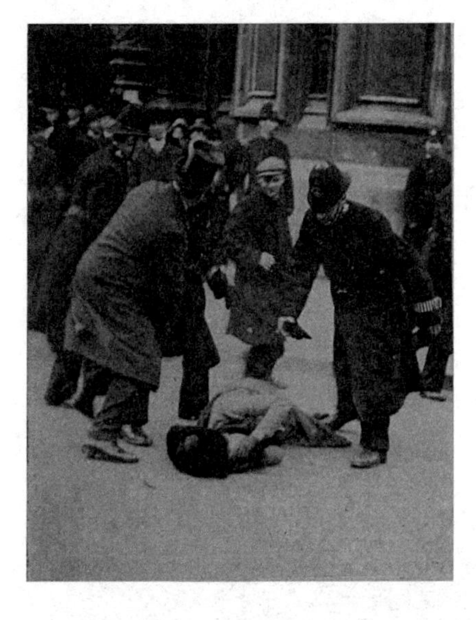

This was a battlefield. Women battered and bloody were being trampled under the hooves of horses, jeered at and taunted by the police, and manhandled in the most obscene way. Those who chained themselves to railings were a target for men grabbing at their breasts or pulling their clothes up. Sylvia Pankhurst recalled: 'The cry went round: "Be careful; they are dragging women down the side streets!" We knew this always meant greater ill-usage.'

Bystanders challenged the police. If the women were breaking the law why didn't they simply arrest them without the brutality? And if their actions were legal, why weren't they allowed through?

Mrs Pankhurst was eventually escorted into the Houses of Parliament, to be told by Asquith's secretary that he wouldn't see her. Over 300 women had faced the brutality of the police only for Asquith to turn them away yet again. For six hours the women kept up the siege of the House of Commons until Parliament Square blazed red with the sunset.

The post-mortem encompassed all emotions. Sylvia was moved to say: 'Never in all the attempts which we have made to carry our deputations to the Prime Minister, have I seen so much bravery on the part of the women and so much violent brutality on the part of the policemen in uniforms, and some men in plainclothes.' Even a parliamentary investigation concluded: 'We cannot resist the conclusion that the police as a whole were under the impression that their duty was not merely to frustrate the attempts of the women to reach the House of Commons, but also to terrorise them in the process. They used in numerous instances excessive violence, which was at once deliberate and aggressive, and was intended to inflict injury. They frequently handled the women with gross indecency.'

Two women died of their injuries that day. Another, Mary Clarke, was arrested for breaking windows and sent to Holloway Prison, where she endured a hunger-strike and force-feeding. She was released, but on Christmas Eve was found unconscious, dying soon afterwards from a burst blood vessel on the brain, probably a result of being force-fed. It was a bitter personal blow for Emmeline Pankhurst. She had lost her sister.

Suffragettes waiting to be sentenced outside Bow Street Court

The sombre group gathered in Marie Newby's drawing room would have recognised several names on the long list of those detained. Among them were Vera Wentworth and Elsie Howey, the Exeter Hunger Strikers, and Helen Craggs, someone who no more than a couple of months earlier had been selling *Votes for Women* alongside them on the streets of Ilfracombe. And there was someone else on the list, unknown to the women as yet, but soon to make her impact in North Devon - Kitty Marion.

More than a hundred women were brought before Bow Street Magistrates the following morning. But, instead of the prison sentence they were prepared for, the order came for them to be released. It was unprecedented. Questions flew around the courtroom. Why? Who made the decision?

The answer soon came. Winston Churchill, then Home Secretary, had decided that conviction was not in the public interest. It was so transparent as to be laughable. Events labelled 'Black Friday' by the press had become a public relations disaster for the Government. With another election in the offing the releases were pure expediency, a move to cut off the suffragettes' oxygen of publicity.

But the women were not done yet. Asquith promised another statement to Parliament on the following Tuesday. At noon the women again gathered at Caxton Hall, every seat full, every balcony, gangway and corridor, crowded ... waiting.

Mrs Pankhurst finally took to the stage, Asquith's statement in her hand. She read: 'The Government will, if they are still in power, give facilities in the next Parliament for effectively proceeding with a Bill which is so framed as to admit of free amendment.'

There was a strained silence as the women struggled to digest Asquith's words. There was no immediate commitment to the Suffrage Bill, not even a commitment for the next session but for 'next Parliament'. And women's suffrage was not to be an integral part of a Bill but left to the mercy of an amendment! Another worthless pledge to add to the list. Christabel leapt to her feet. It was a mockery! An insult to common sense! 'Negotiations are over,' she proclaimed. 'War is declared.'

The women immediately set off towards Downing Street. The police rushed to form a cordon, stretching two-deep across the road, but Mrs Pankhurst didn't slacken her pace. Evelina Haverfield urged the group forward shouting, 'Shove along, girls!' until the cordon broke. Some managed to get to the Prime Minister's door chanting, 'Mr Asquith, give us the Bill, the whole Bill and nothing but the Bill!' Police reinforcements piled in, thrusting the women back. And not just thrusting. Arms and wrists were wrenched and twisted, women were struck about the head and kicked when they were down. Some were trampled and crushed when others fell on top. Protests continued through the night with cabinet ministers' homes and Downing Street targeted for window smashing.

Over 150 women were arrested and brought before Sir Albert de Rutzen at Bow Street Court the following morning. But again, the instruction came from Churchill. All charges of simple obstruction were to be withdrawn. De Rutzen protested, but 106 women were discharged, leaving only those charged with assault and wilful damage to be brought before him: one of them was Evelina Haverfield.

Albert de Rutzen addressed the dock: 'Your case, Mrs Haverfield, appears to be a little worse than the rest. When the Constable intervenes and takes you in to custody, you strike him in the face, and for a moment or two he is scarcely able to see you, and when you are charged you say that the next time you come you will come with a revolver, that is what you said. You are charged with assault. I fine you £5 or, in default, one month.' Evelina was defiant: 'May I say that my whole attitude is a protest against the way the police were instructed to treat our women on Friday. It was the most monstrous thing I have ever known, and when I say I will take a revolver I mean that I will carry on this agitation when I come out of prison with more vigour than ever. We shall carry our point, sir, with all respect to you I am bound to make my protest.'

HIDE-AND-SEEK.

HARASSED ENUMERATOR: "Dear me! I feel sure there are some of those wretched suffragettes living in this house, but hanged if I can find 'em."

Chapter 6
A Barnstaple Sleep-over
Winter 1910 - Spring 1911

London was a turning point for the fledgling Ilfracombe group. Horrified by the scenes outside Parliament, women rushed to join them. Almost immediately there was a call to action when Asquith announced another election, the second within a year. Braunton Literary Debating Society organised a timely meeting on 'Should Women have the Vote?' prompting Mr Mortlock Brown to write to *The North Devon Journal*. 'I appeal to working men of Devon to come to the help of women in the approved Constitutional way by making active support of Woman Suffrage a binding condition on the candidate for his vote.'

The suffragettes homed in on Mid Devon again but the WSPU wasn't the only organisation in town. The NUWSS, the body Emmeline Pankhurst had broken from in frustration at its ineffective campaigning, was extending its reach in South Devon through the energetic work of Marguerite Norma-Smith. She had established branches in Exeter, Sidmouth, Teignmouth, Ottery St Mary and Topsham, alongside the Three Towns and District group already active in Plymouth and Torquay with Dr Mabel Ramsay at the helm. Dr Ramsay was a dedicated and resourceful advocate of the cause. During the winter of 1910-1911 every debating society but one in Plymouth refused to debate Women's Suffrage. But she was up for the challenge, administering, as Miss Norma-Smith put it, 'a Suffrage pill well wrapped in jam in the form of a lecture on Florence Nightingale.'

In December 1910, Marguerite Norma-Smith was also intent on campaigning in Mid Devon but with different methods, a different aim and more than a little apprehension. She arrived in Newton Abbot, where Mrs Pankhurst had previously been attacked, on the day before the Christmas market, 'which, I was told, was the busiest day in the year. All the country people for miles round flock in to the town. It seemed a splendid opportunity for sending our message to all the farms and hamlets in this scattered country district. By means of a wagonette, which was put in the Market Square at 12 o'clock with a placard fastened on to it, I advertised a meeting at 3.30. Miss Allen of Teignmouth very kindly came at short notice and supported me. When we arrived in the Market Square a large and expectant crowd was waiting. We went rather in fear and trembling, as the only open-air Suffrage meeting that has been held in Newton Abbot was when Mrs Pankhurst was thrown down by the crowd, her wagonette run in to the river and the window of her lodgings broken, and she herself had to be rescued by the police.

'Miss Allen opened the meeting. The crowd at first was not inclined to be very friendly but when they realised, after much telling, that we were not militant or against the government, they were prepared to listen. The interruptions were so frequent, however, that a speech became impossible and the meeting took the form of answers to innumerable questions. The crowd grew in numbers till there were between 500 and 600 people. The questions showed a genuine interest and a real desire to understand. The audience grew more and more friendly until finally they asked for another meeting at night - which I promised to give, but unfortunately, the torrents of rain which came cleared the streets. We parted in a friendly spirit and I look forward to having more meetings in Newton Abbot a little later.'

Miss Norma-Smith's 'much telling' that they were not militant or anti-government saved the day. The NUWSS acknowledged that militancy had brought more life to the campaign than their forty-five years of peaceful agitation, but saw it as a trap. 'We regard some of the members of the Cabinet as little better than agents provocateurs and we are sorry to see women fall into the trap. We conceive one Minister, at least, as rubbing his hands in glee at the success of his plot.' For them, orderly propaganda and public discussion was the way forward, not militancy; and backing for candidates pledged to support women's suffrage more effective than a blanket opposition of all Liberals.

But it was the WSPU's tactics that carried the day when the results were announced. In Torquay, Mid Devon, Tavistock and the two Plymouth seats, the Liberals were all ousted. Exeter was on a knife-edge, in more ways than one. Duke, the Conservative, actually told May Montague and the rest of the Exeter WSPU delegation that he wouldn't include a pledge for woman suffrage in his election address. But the Pankhursts were adamant - all Liberal candidates were to be opposed. So, incredibly, they still campaigned for him. On the day, they celebrated success by the narrowest of margins. Duke held his seat by one vote. But their celebrations were short-lived. An appeal by the Liberal, St Maur, was upheld. The seat was his.

Across the country, the WSPU kept the Liberals out in up to forty seats, playing their part in ensuring another hung Parliament. In one sense it was an astounding achievement. This was a time when ladies were expected to confine themselves to the parlour and polite conversation, not make an exhibition of themselves accosting law-abiding Gentlemen on the streets. But having crossed that divide they demonstrated their ability to organise, campaign and challenge with ruthless efficiency.

Politically, it was a case of 'here we go again,' particularly when the new Parliament of 1911 saw yet another Private Member's Suffrage Bill. This time the intention was to give every woman householder the vote. As always, only one thing could stop it; time, or the lack of it. Given Asquith's track record this felt inevitable. But the women seemed to have developed collective amnesia. They again became relentlessly optimistic. Christabel sent out a rallying cry for women to work for this Bill as they'd never worked before. This time they would succeed. The public were with them, a majority of MPs were with them, what could possibly go wrong?

One person who could always be relied on to respond to Christabel's rallying call was Annie Kenney. She was about to bring the big guns to North Devon. The instruction came to book halls in Barnstaple and Ilfracombe for one of the most significant speakers in the organisation, Frederick Pethick-Lawrence. His credentials were impeccable ... barrister, economist, mathematician and, together with his wife, Emmeline, a core supporter of the WSPU. He'd written on women's suffrage, co-edited *Votes for Women,* posted bail for women and bankrolled the organisation.

Suddenly it was all hands to the pump, confirming the Gaiety Hall in Ilfracombe and the Imperial in Barnstaple, addressing envelopes for handbills and sending out invitations to anyone from Braunton to Torrington.

The day arrived and at Barnstaple the hall was full. Annie set out her stall, emphasising the non-party stance of the WSPU. If the present government refused them the franchise the next would, 'continue to receive their attentions.' She stressed they were not asking that all women should have the vote: 'But it is only right and just that all those who pay rates and taxes should have it. Lunatics, criminals, aliens, children paupers ... and women are disenfranchised. A state of affairs that is foolish, unreasonable, illogical and bad for the country. Our demands are moderate. Last year a Conciliation Bill was proposed ... this would have meant there would be one million women voters to seven and a half million men - not a great revolution.' Annie continued to regale her audience with an account of the benefits countries experienced where women had the franchise, then took on those who claimed that women were not as intelligent and well-educated as men. '74,000 men voted at the recent election who could not write their names!'

It was a stirring lead-in to the star turn of the evening, Frederick Pethick-Lawrence: 'It is very wrong,' he said, 'that only one-half of mankind should be concerned in guiding the destinies of the State.' He dwelt on the inadequacies of a male-dominated state in dealing with the deplorable social conditions of the poor, the sick, the young: 'Women have not been allowed to exercise their judgement in these matters and their point of view has not been listened to ... What women want is the driving power that only the vote will give.'

He spoke of the dire working conditions of women and families struggling to survive in slums and the unacceptable rate of infant mortality - 110 of every 1,000 babies died in the first year - an eye-opener for many in this rural audience who had no idea of conditions in the cities. 'It is a state of affairs,' he said with complete confidence, 'that will be remedied when women get the vote.' Frederick Pethick-Lawrence pleaded with his listeners, most of whom had never been to a Suffrage meeting before, not to believe everything they read in the press: 'The real facts ... are very different. The women have great cause for complaint on account of the treatment they have received ... Great physical force has been used against the women and they have only replied with the force they consider absolutely necessary to repel that used against them.' He urged everyone to become readers of *Votes for Women*. It was an unmissable opportunity to plug the paper. Marie, Anne and others rushed to make copies available, keen to advertise their latest fund-raiser, Self Denial week:

> March 11th - Self Denial week comes at a most opportune moment as money is needed to carry on local work. It is hoped that all will take part in a special scheme of canvassing. Names of those willing to help should be sent in at once to the Hon Sec. Splendid reports were given by all the local papers of the recent meetings.
>
> March 17th - an enjoyable members' meeting was held last week, the subjects under discussion being Self Denial Week and Census evasion, the members present promising to do their best to collect money during Self Denial week.
>
> March 24th - many thanks to the members who collected for Self Denial week. New sympathisers were gained and many papers sold. Will helpers come forward and assist the Hon Sec by taking a few copies of the paper each week round to some of the shops and houses. The sale of *Votes for Women* must be increased. It is so important that the public should learn the truth of the movement.

This two-pronged focus on spreading the word and fundraising was central to the WSPU. Self Denial Week became a regular feature with women urged to give something up and send the money saved to the fund. One suggestion was to go for a few days without a servant. Only in the WSPU! It may have bolstered the coffers but it wasn't such great news for servants struggling to make ends meet without their usual wages.

The week was organised with impeccable efficiency from the WSPU headquarters in London. With over a hundred paid workers it's no wonder there was such pressure to fundraise. But money

wasn't needed just for staff. They had speakers travelling to all parts of the country handing out hundreds of thousands of leaflets. Funds were needed to pay for trains, hire halls, print material and publicise their campaigns. And a once-in-a-decade opportunity to get their message across was on the horizon. The WSPU was about to organise a mass sleep-over.

1911 was census year and The Women's Freedom League was urging a boycott with the slogan: 'Since women do not count neither will they be counted'. Women had a choice, they said: to comply, to evade by absenting themselves from home, or to resist by defacing their returns. There was plenty of encouragement to evade. A programme of dances and whist drives, all night meetings in public halls or houses and more was being organised across the country.

London was the mecca for making a night of it. A midnight promenade was arranged for Trafalgar Square followed by entertainment at the Scala Theatre and skating at the rink in Kingsway to live music. As always, the WSPU thought of everything. The Gardenia restaurant, next to Drury Lane Theatre, was booked to provide refreshments through the night.

Anne Ball made her choice. As everyone gathered in her sitting room on March 17th she announced she was opening up The Trained Nurses' Institute in Ashleigh Road, Barnstaple for anyone who wanted to evade the census. She would resist by spoiling her return, a tactic hundreds adopted nationwide, scrawling 'Votes for Women' or 'No Vote No Census' instead of entering information. It was inspired. As a businesswoman Anne couldn't risk arrest but now she had found a way of protesting that would strike at the very heart of government.

On the evening of Sunday 2nd April, Marie, Margaret and others from Ilfracombe and Barnstaple make their way to Ashleigh Road, pausing in the shadows to check they are unobserved before hastening up the path to slip into the muted glow of the hallway. They carry baskets of food, contributions to the supper party their hostess has arranged. Less usual are the rugs and pillows wedged under their arms. Inside they are greeted by earlier arrivals, sharing an air of suppressed excitement, of conspiracy and daring. After all, they are about to become law-breakers!

Inside Nurse Ball's drawing room, the ladies make themselves comfortable on couches, tucked up with books in their laps, or making a four at the card table. All gratefully accept the cups of tea and biscuits handed round by Nurse Simes and enjoy easy conversation, interspersed with nervous laughter as they recall tense moments with husbands and fathers persuaded, or coerced, into conspiring with them. On a small table at the entrance is a census form with NO VOTE NO CENSUS emblazoned across the orderly columns. Beside it, a dish with a neat sign inviting contributions to the £5 fine. Nurse Ball will shoulder the legal implications; the least others can do is share the financial penalty.

A bridge tournament gets underway, the evening almost eerily normal apart from a creeping tiredness and Anne's constant adjustment of the drapes to prevent any light seeping into the street. Seeing lights through the night isn't so unusual for a nursing home, but they don't want to advertise themselves, not yet anyway.

A midnight supper is laid out in the dining room and a toast to the WSPU enthusiastically made by all. As they clear the food and dishes there's a camaraderie in the air; friends and acquaintances sharing a common, illicit, purpose. This is the first time the fledgling group has taken any direct action. They may not be suffering the blows of oppression outside the Houses of Parliament, or the degradation of Holloway, but they have taken a giant stride outside of convention. Their lives will never be the same again.

As night draws on they prepare for sleep. There are one or two beds for the more elderly ladies but most help to lift the couches back against the wall to create space on the floor. Blankets and rugs are laid down as makeshift mattresses and pulled up over fully clothed bodies. Some women are happy to cluster together. Others, like Cerisa Palmer, claim their own space by turning towards the wall. But no-one expects to sleep. Many talk to pass a restless night and, for some, reservations creep in as spirits wane.

'Did you read the dialogue in The Times?' someone asks, 'between those pro and anti our protest? They describe it as nothing more than a nursery fit of bad temper and a crime against science!'

'What nonsense.'

'They say Lloyd George had a radical programme of health and social reform planned for the Liberals and how can he achieve that without the information he needs to plan for better conditions for everyone?'

'Have you read the questions? Wanting to know all about us as wives and mothers. More state surveillance than social data collection if you want my opinion.' Marie has no doubts. But others are not so sure.

'But can breaking the law ever be justified? Perhaps the NUWSS are right, perhaps it is better to make our point in ways that don't antagonise the politicians and the public.'

'Don't you know?' Marie says. 'The NUWSS are joining in tonight. Dr Ramsay has opened her home in Plymouth. At this very moment they will be elegantly strewn across her drawing room floor just like us.' There's a moment's silence before laughter catches hold of the women one by one. 'What reforms have ever been gained without mass protests, all of them breaking the law in one way or another? Why should it be any different for women? If becoming a law-breaker is the only way to achieve publicity and force change then it is our moral duty to act. Just wait for the morning papers. Our protest will be all across them.'

As morning dawns, the women set about restoring the nursing home to its former orderliness. But even those who leave take care not to arrive home before noon, the witching hour for being counted. The same day, the enumerator calls to collect Nurse Ball's return. She hands him the sheet with 'No Vote, no Census,' clearly printed across it .

'What is this, Nurse Ball?'

'It is my return,' she replies.

'How many persons were resident here last night?'

'I refuse to answer any questions.'

'And I must insist, Nurse Ball.'

'And I decline to answer.'

'Come now, Nurse Ball, I am duty bound to report this to the registrar who will then report it to his superior officers. We don't want that that do we?'

'That is exactly what I want.'

The number of women who refused to complete the census was reported to the cabinet. At the stroke of a pen, Nurse Ball's protest reached the heart of government. And she had another, very public, protest in mind.

Chapter Seven
Pay the Piper; Call the Tune!
Spring 1911

Women contributed over twenty million pounds a year towards the country's economy. But without the vote they had absolutely no say in how that twenty million was spent. It was unjust. It was indefensible. And in 1909 a group of suffragists decided enough was enough. 'No Taxation Without Representation' became the clarion call of the Women's Tax Resistance League (WTRL).

The idea was the inspiration of Dora Montefiore, who took resistance a stage further. 'When talking this over ... with Theresa Billington and Annie Kenney, I told them that now we had the organisation of the WSPU to back me up I would, if it were thought advisable, not only refuse to pay income tax, but would shut and bar my doors and keep out the bailiff, so as to give the demonstration more publicity and thus help to educate public opinion about the fight for the political emancipation of women which was going on ... At one time my housekeeper and I counted no less than twenty-two pressmen outside the house ... '

'No vote, no tax' was also embraced by someone who was becoming increasingly familiar in North Devon, Lady Evelina Haverfield. She was a WTRL committee member and the person who most likely encouraged Anne Ball to join their ranks. This Anne did with a personal letter to Lloyd George explaining that she wasn't willing to pay anything until he granted women the vote. It probably followed the lines of a letter from another tax resister: 'Taxation without representation is tyranny, and although we have to submit to the tyranny, we are not prepared to subscribe to maintain it. To force women out of their earnings to pay salaries to Cabinet Ministers and MPs to legislate for men, who through the ballot box, command attention and consideration is to me such a gross injustice that I offer no apology for my action.'

Official letters dropped on the doormat of the Nursing Home in response to Anne's letter, culminating in a final demand from the Inland Revenue. This was her cue for a reply explaining her refusal to pay - and the point of no return. It was not an easy decision. Nurse Ball was a respected businesswoman in Barnstaple and Ilfracombe. She relied on the goodwill of local people to patronise her Trained Nurses' Establishments. Together with being labelled a Census resister, this action marked her out as a law breaker, potentially undermining her standing in the two towns. Yet she still posted her final statement ... and waited.

Just two weeks after the excitement of Census night, she opened the door to some very different callers. Bailiffs had a legal right to enter a resister's property to take items to cover the tax owed, plus enough to cover their costs. Fortunately many were sensitive about this ultimate intrusion. Items were generally agreed upon, so Anne would have directed them to the canteen of cutlery and a few selected silver pieces identified as being of sufficient value. Slowly, the tally would be made and her goods removed.

Nurse Anne Ball alongside the confiscated items.

Having made her stand, Anne's next move was to attract as much publicity for the cause as possible by advertising the sales of her goods, reaching people who wouldn't have dreamt of attending a women's suffrage meeting. She achieved at least one report in the North Devon Journal:

> VOTES FOR WOMEN
> NOVEL PROTEST AT BARNSTAPLE
>
> Miss Ball of the Nursing Homes at Ashleigh-road, Barnstaple and Larkstone, Ilfracombe, who is the Hon. Literary Secretary of the Ilfracombe branch of the Women's Social and Political Union, recently refused a demand for Imperial taxes as a protest against the exclusion of women from the privilege of the vote, and she

> wrote to the Chancellor of the Exchequer announcing that she would not be willing pay the taxes until women's suffrage had been granted. But taxes *have* to be paid, despite conscientious objections, and so in this case the usual steps to enforce payment were made. A sufficient number of goods to cover the amount due were seized at the Ashleigh-road Nursing Home and an auction for their sale was conducted on Tuesday morning by Mr T. W. Sanders at the offices of Messrs. Sanders and Son, High-street. The proceedings lasted only a few minutes, the articles (silver and cutlery) being quickly purchased by lady friends who accompanied Miss Ball to the sale. The net result of the protest is that Miss Ball has to pay the amount claimed, plus £1 5s expenses. But Miss Ball is confident that the cause she has so much at heart will be advanced by the procedure.

Marie and others showed solidarity, attending the auction and bidding on items in turn until all Anne Ball's possessions had been restored to her. It was to become a familiar pattern.

As well as direct action, the Ilfracombe group kept up the pressure with letters to the editor of the *North Devon Journal* using the pen name, *Suum Cuique* - to give to each their own. 'There are indications in your paper of late that North Devon takes more than a secondary interest in this subject,' *Suum Cuique* observes before promising to 'send letters for discussion for the benefit of those who retain an open mind.'

They began by tackling the arguments for women suffrage. Namely, if sex was no disability with taxation then neither should it be with representation in the form of the vote. No argument there. Furthermore, women were excluded because of their alleged physical and mental inferiority but physical differences were not unique to women: 'A woman may be stronger than a boy, a man than a woman, a labourer than a bank clerk, and pugilist than either.' They also dismiss the idea of the intellectual inferiority of women - based on the theory that the brain of a woman differed anatomically from the brain of a man. 'As this theory has been disproved, and no difference has ever been found to exist between the male and the female brain there is no need of discussion this point.' They summarise: 'Woman suffrage is claiming ... justice in accordance with two prevailing principles ... "No taxation without representation" and "woman is not inferior to man in body, mind, nor spirit."'

This letter was followed by a lengthy piece in April taking up three full columns. Headed 'The Woman Suffrage Movement', *Suum Cuique* included a table of societies representing the full strength of the movement. It's an impressive summary. *Suum Cuique* concludes: 'I must reserve for another letter some observations on this goodly show, and will now merely emphasise the fact that one common object has brought these Societies into existence, that common object being to obtain for women the Parliamentary Franchise on the same terms as it is, or may be, granted to men, and to establish equity of rights between the sexes.'

It remained a much needed campaign. Woman suffrage had been debated in the Commons no less than twenty times before 1911. Twelve Bills were brought before the House. Six passed a second reading. None had become law.

Chapter Eight
Loud and Proud in London
Spring into Summer 1911

Bolstered by the success of their census and tax resistance protests, the Ilfracombe and Barnstaple group escalated their activity. Marie, Anne and Nurse Simes, a new member who was becoming increasingly active, began leafleting door-to-door. It was a brave move in this small community where many were adamant that a woman's place was in the home as a wife and mother. Especially where the husband held such an important role as Dr Newby did as surgeon at the Cottage Hospital. It was unthinkable that any woman could disrespect her husband's authority by handing out subversive literature in this way. Marie would have had doors shut in her face, been given the cold-shoulder at church and become the butt of hostile gossip. It's a testament to her convictions that she refused to be silenced.

The group persevered, doing their best to persuade shopkeepers in Ilfracombe High Street to sell copies of *Votes for Women*. And they had the increasingly proactive backing of Annie Kenney. On April 21st, Anne Ball's drawing room was crowded as Annie took the floor. She was on good form, speaking for ninety minutes on why women householders should have the vote. She carried her audience with her in a passionate bid for everyone to involve themselves in the cause in whatever way they could. Would they write immediately to Sir Godfrey Baring [their Liberal candidate] asking him to support the latest Suffrage Bill? Would they vote with their feet and show North Devon's solidarity with the movement at the demonstration planned for June 17th in London? And would they join Mrs Pankhurst at a meeting in the Albert Hall afterwards? (Tickets available but going fast).

It was a pivotal moment. The second reading of the Suffrage Bill had passed with an overwhelming majority and the government were considering whether or not to grant further time for it. Now was the time to overwhelm Asquith with demands that he progress the Bill.

It was a stirring call to action for the existing WSPU members and enough to persuade five more to join, including a ninety-five year old lady. *The Ilfracombe Gazette* had a unique take on the meeting: 'With great power and knowledge of her subject, Miss Annie Kenney spoke on the Women's Suffrage Bill now before Parliament. Really though, if women eventually obtain that much craved boon, the franchise, will not the first few general elections at which they exercise their right to vote be highly reminiscent of Gilbertian opera?' Perhaps it was this comment that inspired 'a member of the WSPU' to respond:

Sir, I have just returned from a political meeting at which the women were urged to use their influence over men, what we suffragists call the 'backstair influence'. How weak men must be if they can be so easily persuaded for whom to vote! … No doubt a few women use the charm of their sex to influence men to their way of thinking, or wives importune their husbands till for very weariness these are induced to vote against their judgement. This kind of influence is, in my opinion quite illegitimate and will become, one hopes, more rare when women have some real political power of their own … On Friday May 5th, the Woman Suffrage Bill is to be introduced by Sir George Kemp for its second reading, and will probably pass as it did last year, by a large majority … If facilities are granted to enable the Bill to become law this Session, then women will have a legitimate power of their own.

Inspired by Annie, the group committed to join the June 17th procession in London. Anne Ball was in charge of the excursion details. The West of England was to be well represented, with women from Bristol, Bath, Bridgwater, Cornwall, Crediton, Devizes, Exeter, Honiton, Paignton, Plymouth, and Torquay as well as Ilfracombe. In addition to the practical arrangements there were rehearsals to arrange - for the song. *March of the Women*, a specially composed piece, was to be sung throughout the demonstration and learning it by heart was obligatory!

The timing for the procession was perfect. George V's coronation was scheduled for June 22nd, just six days later. People were gathering in London from all over the Commonwealth; it was a once in a lifetime opportunity to show the whole world the strength and determination of the movement in the UK. Women in Australia and New Zealand already had the vote. If they could be represented, why not women from the birthplace of the Empire? Every suffrage society in the country was planning to be there; the WSPU, the NUWSS, the Women's Freedom League, churches, actresses, writers, graduates, Young Suffrage League and more. It was to be a mass celebration of the sisterhood of women. And the first procession since the Ilfracombe suffragettes had become an official group. Nothing was going to keep them from saying loud and proud that Devon was part of the movement.

But first there was the small matter of yet another election. Barely six months after Sir Ernest Soares renewed his pledge to represent the Barnstaple constituency, he resigned. There were rumours of ill health but then news filtered through that he had been appointed the new Assistant Comptroller of the National Debt Office. It was enough to ruffle some feathers. There was innuendo about jobs for the boys in Parliament. How had he been appointed over the heads of better qualified civil servants? Did he take a medical? If so did he pass it? Questions all neatly sidestepped by Asquith.

Whatever the truth of it, another by-election was inevitable. It was the last thing anyone had an appetite for. But there was no slacking for Marie and Anne. At 8pm on Friday 21st April, they dutifully joined the crowds filtering into the Alexandra Hall at Ilfracombe for some reconnaissance on Sir Godfrey Baring, the new Liberal candidate. Probably the first thing to strike them was the shaggy moustache that seemed compulsory for every politician at the time. It squirmed as he addressed the audience on Irish Home Rule, the Parliament Bill and how he most certainly wasn't a Hottentot! But not a word on Women's suffrage, a red rag to a bull for Marie. It was time to draft in some significant backup.

A few days later a car drew up outside the Newby's semi-detached villa in Broad Park Avenue. The Honourable Evelina Haverfield had arrived. Driving the car was a face familiar from the pages of *Votes for Women* - Vera Holme, a mounted Marshall with Evelina at last year's procession and Mrs Pankhurst's chauffeur.

It was no hardship for Evelina to motor down to North Devon. For many years she had been close friends with Ethel Acland Hood, originally from St Audries in West Quantoxhead. A few years earlier Ethel had moved to Brendon, a small village between Lynton and Porlock, and was undoubtedly the connection that brought Evelina to this remote Devon outpost. Evelina acquired a cottage nestling beside the path to Rockford on the north of the East Lyn river, immediately re-naming it Peace Cottage. The location was perfect. When not campaigning, Evelina loved to ride; to be so close to the open country of Exmoor and able to join the Somerset and North Devon Staghounds was all she could ask for.

Her stays at Peace Cottage were mostly for high days and holidays, although that was to change when her relationship with Vera Holme became more intimate. Annie Kenney's fondness for her female companions was only the tip of the iceberg when it came to relationships within the WSPU. In the privacy of Peace Cottage, Evelina set up home with Vera. It was a discreet relationship, although perhaps it wasn't wise to carve their initials on their bed then ask the landlord of the Staghunters Inn to look after it when they left a few years later.

Having Evelina local was a great boost for the Ilfracombe group, particularly when it came to confronting the candidates. On Tuesday, May 2nd, Evelina joined Marie to drive over to Bideford for an assignation of a different kind. They had an appointment with Mr Parker, the Conservative candidate, at his committee rooms in Appledore. Judging by a report in the Bideford Gazette, it was a worthwhile trip: 'The Hon. Mrs Haverfield, of the Women's Social and Political Union, who was one of the ladies who interviewed the candidate, told the press representative that Mr Parker said he was prepared to go as far as Mr Balfour (the previous candidate) had gone hitherto on the subject of women's suffrage, and was also prepared to mention this subject when speaking in public.' Something of a concession but not exactly a ringing endorsement of votes for women.

They moved on to Sir Godfrey Baring who, Evelina said: 'had a very good understanding of the subject, and was ready to vote straight for any Suffrage Bill which went before the House, and press for facilities as far as he could, without voting against his own Government.' A more hopeful response, although of course, he was a Liberal, so they wouldn't be supporting him.

But Sir Godfrey Baring did have the support of another familiar face. May 4th saw the return of Sir Frank Newnes to North Devon to speak at a rally at Lynton Town Hall. Bob Jones, in the chair was effusive with his welcome: 'All honour is due to wealthy gentlemen such as the late deeply revered Sir George Newnes, who was Lynton's greatest benefactor - (Cheers) and Sir Frank Newnes whom we are all glad to see on a Liberal platform in Lynton (Cheers), our late member, Sir Ernest Soares (Cheers) and our future member Sir Godfrey Baring (Cheers). F.D. Ackland, whose grandfather and great-grandfather had both represented the Barnstaple Division in Parliament, was in full flow on the success of Liberal policies when Sir Godfrey burst into the hall, arriving hotfoot from speaking at Brendon - perhaps after enduring more than a little heckling from

Evelina and Vera. In Lynton the audience leapt to its feet and immediately started singing 'For he's a jolly good fellow.'

He gave a rousing speech citing Lynton as a radical Liberal stronghold and asking them to send him to Parliament as an ardent and convinced Liberal who believed that the work of Liberalism was only just beginning. He left the hall to loud cheers, en route to address meetings at Parracombe and Arlington. Sir Frank Newnes took the floor to move the motion that: 'this meeting heartily endorses the candidature of Sir Godfrey Baring for the Barnstaple Division of Devon and hereby pledges to support him at the poll.'

Returning just a few weeks before Hollerday House and its contents were to be auctioned was poignant for Frank Newnes: 'I am very glad indeed once more to be among my friends in Lynton (Cheers) ... You all know that the desire and endeavour of my father all the years that he lived at Lynton was to be the friend of everybody (Applause) I want to maintain this. I have known most of you here a great many years, almost since I was a boy, and I believe a man has a right to stand up for his political principles ... I am prouder of being a Liberal than ever I was.' His words received a ringing endorsement with this audience but lodged with others in a quite different way.

The NUWSS took advantage of the election campaign to make inroads into North Devon. In just two-and-a-half days Marguerite Norma-Smith, the Devon and Cornwall organiser, addressed eight large gatherings in different parts of the constituency. She drove between meetings in a car decorated with red, white and green, the NUWSS colours, and displaying a large placard on the back. She obviously made an impact, recording that people living in the country villages realised for the first time that Women's Suffrage was a living movement.

> On Wednesday evening we had a large open-air meeting in the Square in Barnstaple, the first that had been held in the town. Although the party feeling was very intense and the town very excited, we were treated with the utmost good feeling from first to last, and listened to with genuine interest. At 12.30 on

Thursday we held a meeting at Lynton. The audience there was mostly composed of men who showed their approval and appreciation throughout my speech and one announced at the end of the meeting: "Miss, you have talked more sense to-day than all the men who have been down here electioneering." We drove away happy that a statement of our case had made such a good impression.

By 2.30 we were at Coombe Martin, a long straggling village. Our car soon brought the village women out of their houses and they listened for the first time to an explanation of the meaning of our movement. At 4.30 we held a large and enthusiastic meeting in the main street in Ilfracombe. A drunken man was a little troublesome but the people were so keen to hear that they effectively silenced him. Questions were asked and answered and literature given away, and the people cheered us as we left. At night we had another meeting in Barnstaple.

On Friday we visited the western half of the constituency and had a splendid meeting in Bideford, where we again drove away amidst cheering and the waving of hats. In Appledore we had a mixed audience of townspeople and fishermen. When I asked for questions, a man remarked, "There is nothing to say: it is all so plain and straight-forward". The vicar of the town, who stood in the crowd to listen, came and spoke to me at the end and said he was "entirely in agreement with our whole movement." In the evening again we had a still larger meeting in Barnstaple and a lively discussion followed.

It may have all been 'so plain and straightforward' but when Godfrey Baring won the by-election it signalled business as usual in more ways than one. Baring even swopped homes with Ernest Soares, moving into Upcott House just outside Barnstaple. He visited Ilfracombe a few weeks later boasting that the Conservatives would never get as near them again as they just had. But Marie and Evelina's interviews had been timely. When the second reading of the latest incarnation of the Suffrage Bill came before Parliament, Sir

Godfrey voted for the motion, just one of an overwhelming majority in favour.

The women of Ilfracombe were denied a say in the election of their MP but the second week of May saw many of them casting their vote in the district council elections. Of 1,639 voters, 355 were women. Equality was still some way off though; the women were allocated a separate voting station in the Alexandra Hall.

It had been an eventful twelve months for the North Devon suffragettes with three elections, two Suffrage Bills, endless procrastination from the Prime Minister, several blistering talks from Annie Kenney, the official launch of the Ilfracombe and Barnstaple WSPU, the arrival of the NUWSS, an auction and a sleepover. But the icing on the cake was still to come ... the Procession in London on Saturday 17th June.

On Friday 16th, Ilfracombe members were busy distributing handbills and posters so locals not fortunate enough to see the Procession would at least know all about it. The leadership of the WSPU were in no doubt about the importance of the event: 'The Great Procession of Women ... will be the most memorable which has ever taken place in history. It will stretch for seven miles in length and will be made up of forty-thousand women who have chosen this method to demonstrate their determination to win the franchise for their sex.'

Participation demanded dedication. Workers were tasked with organising the women into sections, each under the command of a marshal. Teams of volunteers advertised the event, distributing thousands of handbills and chalking pavements, including the whole of the route of the procession. The familiar figure of Helen

Craggs was in charge of the *Votes for Women* Corps, selling the magazine throughout the day. They were phenomenally successful, selling over 10,000 copies. There was also copious guidance for the marchers.

'Don't ... wear gowns that have to be held up; be later than 4.30 in joining the Procession; leave your ranks once you have taken your place; look behind once the Procession has started; wave handkerchiefs; break line; break step; crowd up if the ranks in front of you are halted; run to catch up the line in front.

'Do ... wear white if possible, with a gay display of the colours; wear your badge; wear a small hat and no long hat pins; be punctual; take up your place five abreast in the Procession and remain there; bring some provision lest you suffer from want of food; leave a clear space in front and behind every banner; keep step with the marcher on the left; march eyes front like a soldier in the ranks; march with the left foot first; make quite sure you know the Marching Song by heart.

'Do ... realise that the work of the organisation on so enormous a scale would be impossible except for the fact that the WSPU relies on the intelligent, self-restrained and hearty cooperation of each and all its members.'

There were even detailed instructions for turning a corner: 'For a line of five people to turn a corner with neatness and precision is a very difficult achievement which calls for the exercise of great care and attention. Upon its successful accomplishment depends the good effect of the Procession. The person on the inside of the corner should mark time, without advancing at all, the second should advance very slightly, also marking time, the third must take longer steps, the fourth longer steps still and the fifth has to step out and swing round in fine style without for one second breaking the straightness and solidity of the line.'

Fully briefed, as Saturday, June 17th arrived, the Ilfracombe and Barnstaple representatives hurried from Paddington Station to take their place in section A3. To reach their assembly point by Cleopatra's Needle they had to pass a group at the head of the procession representing suffragette prisoners, a spectacle beyond anything they had experienced.

Then came the signal to move. Marie, Anne and their companions advanced, five abreast, part of a mighty stream singing *March of the Women*, faithfully committed to memory.

Life, strife - these two are one,
Naught can ye win but by faith and daring.
On, on - that ye have done
But for the work of to-day preparing.
Firm in reliance, laugh a defiance
Laugh in hope, for sure is the end
March, march, many as one
Shoulder to shoulder, and friend to friend.

Fellow marcher Miss Skrine recorded her experiences in a letter to the *Bath Chronicle:*

There was something unusual about the crowd itself. What was it? Why yes, of course, the colours! They were everywhere. Purple, white and green, gold and white, gold, green and white.

WSPU, Freedom League, Church League, Men's Society, many more still, but everywhere, outnumbering the rest, the red, white and green of the National Union of Women's Suffrage Societies ... So on we went ... wishing we had more time to speak to fellow suffragists from Scotland, Yorkshire, Lancashire, the Midlands, East, West and South ...

Now the stress of the march made itself felt. Up and down the length of Whitehall, through Whitehall Place, Northumberland Avenue, Trafalgar Square, Pall Mall, slowly and with constant halts, the great procession unwound its six miles of orderly length.

It was a new and trying experience, this slow intermittent journey through a lane, sometimes all too narrow, of the watching faces of a great and silent crowd. Their silence struck the attention at once. No cheering yet, no demonstration of enthusiasm - but scarcely an unkind or sneering word. To those among us who had had experience of petition work at the polling booths of 1910 this was indeed a significant fact.

Presently we became conscious of a curious undercurrent of sound among them, a low throbbing, regular beat, like the sound of a tom-tom, the steady clapping of hands from friends who had the courage of their convictions.

Encouragement was indeed welcome, for the physical strain on processionists was severe. The necessity of moving with the muscles braced to halt at any moment, the halts themselves, the long standing and slow marching through the hot airless passage cleared by the police were all exhausting. One could not wonder that some faces grew white and strained ...

As we turned into St James's Street, our case was altered. Here the sunset light from a glorious evening sky lit up the waving banners. A cool breeze brought freshness ... Best of all, our friends had mustered. We knew it in a moment. Silence and attention had meant respect, but from this point on we found enthusiasm. Cheers, clapping, friendly words were heard from every side.

But more was to come. As the golden banners dipped suddenly before a decorated balcony, every right hand was raised to salute a certain grey-haired, sweet-faced lady. For Mrs Wolstenholme Elmy, rising, bent over the parapet, waving white old hands in greeting to these her younger sisters in the cause.

[One of the first women to petition Parliament for the vote almost half a century earlier.]

That was a moment to remember. There came another. When each rank reached the point where Piccadilly sloped downhill, those marching could for the first time see something of the procession they helped to make. That mile-long spectacle of moving banners winding away quite out of sight, and winding as each knew, for twice as far before and behind, must have brought to many a strange moment of realisation. To know oneself less an individual than a living part of a great movement, is an experience which comes to most men at least once in a lifetime. To most women it is denied. But here it came to forty-thousand.

From this point to its goal, the procession swung on at a quicker and therefore easier pace. Everyone was singing now, and everywhere we saw waving handkerchiefs and heard the cheers and clapping of our friends. And so marching, tired but triumphant, we reached the open space behind the Albert Hall ...

To the multitude of Suffragists, who could not be with us, to the innumerable friends who watched us pass, to the processionists themselves has come immense encouragement ...

Finally, has the greatest direct result - the Franchise - been won? At least one influential paper has called the Procession, "The Women's Victory." May that victory, which seems indeed so near as to be almost ours, come without bitterness and further struggle.

Mrs Pankhurst took up the theme when she addressed the sea of white-uniformed women finally gathered inside the Albert Hall: 'What does this demonstration of ours mean? It means victory! And here we are tonight, not only in the sure and certain hope of victory, but with a sure and certain knowledge that victory is very near. We who began as a small insignificant band of women only a few years ago, are now a mighty army, an irresistible force, a force that is bound to win ... because it is an army composed of individuals all animated with a burning desire for freedom.'

It had been a long and exhausting day, but one that Marie, Anne and others in the Ilfracombe and Barnstaple contingent would never forget: a day when a few determined women from a remote Devon community came to know themselves less as individuals 'than a living part of a great movement'.

According to *Votes for Women,* 'On Saturday last all previous records were broken and surpassed. It can be said without fear of contradiction that no such procession ever walked through the streets of London or any city of the world before. Whether it be judged by the standard of the numerical strength, of beauty of design, of enthusiasm, of consummate organisation, the Women's March of Saturday, June 17 will stand out for ever a great event in the history of this world.'

The message was loud and clear.

Women wanted the vote.
Women deserved the vote.
Women must have the vote.

Chapter Nine
Suffragists Make Their Mark
Summer 1911

Ilfracombe vaunted the great procession. Under the headline, *March of the 40,000,* the *Gazette* declared: 'Pageantry, artistic and of high merit, marked the great women's Suffrage demonstration held in London in brilliant sunshine on Saturday. The procession which marched from Victoria Embankment to the Albert Hall was seven miles long and took over two hours to pass…' Ilfracombe Picture Hall put on two showings of the procession. Being in the Hall itself was still a novelty, it had only been open a few months. Whether from the cheap seats at the front or the plush upholstered ones on raised flooring towards the back, everyone had the chance to appreciate the sheer scale and significance of the event.

The Great Procession marked a rite of passage for Marie, Anne and their fellow WSPU members. Ilfracombe now had a fully fledged, fully committed suffragette movement. And there was work to do. 'Miss Ball and Mrs Du Sautoy Newby will give an At Home at the Nursing Home for members and sympathisers tomorrow ... The Women's Great Procession has done much to convert people to the cause.' The meeting was a great success attracting new members, one a Russian lady, and boosting sales of *Votes for Women*.

But their elation was short-lived. Asquith, through the mouthpiece of David Lloyd George, was at it again - but with a new and devious plan. Overnight Lloyd George became the suffragettes' greatest advocate. Of course women deserved the vote, but why stop at the one million the present Bill would enfranchise? If women deserved the vote, as they so patently did, then let six million married women also have it.

Cue thunderous applause for this champion of the women's cause.

Or not.

The Conciliation Committee had laboured long and hard drafting a Bill that stood a chance of being passed by Parliament. They knew that if they demanded all women were enfranchised it would create a backlash amongst MPs. Settling for one million was their best and, for now at least, only hope of the legislation being passed. Lloyd George's amendment would create rebellion, and he knew it. It was a wrecking tactic, pure and simple.

Marie and Anne were quick to respond with a letter to the *Ilfracombe Gazette:* 'The very large procession of women through London recently, and the friendly and respectful attitude of the large crowds who viewed it, show that the determination and unanimity of women are turning the scale of public opinion in their favour. But the wide and sweeping amendments, by altering the reasonable and conciliatory character of the present Bill, will certainly reduce its majority, and thereby leave a loophole for escape from promises.'

It was sabotage in all but name. They appealed to readers to lobby their MP to insist the Bill was passed as it stood: 'The alternative will mean another long round of discussion and delay and for women the certain conviction that they are being played with by the Government ...'

Victory, so certain after the Great Procession, was again on a knife-edge. They had to open the eyes of the women of North Devon to what the government was doing. Two weeks later another letter appeared in Christabel's name: 'Mr Lloyd George, or any other, who asserts that a Bill enfranchising seven million women can be carried ... is obviously throwing dust in the eyes of the women who are waiting so anxiously and working so hard for political enfranchisement ... The pursuit of wrecking tactics by those who seek to deter indefinitely the enfranchisement of women will have the effect of increasing the enthusiasm and energy of those who are endeavouring to get the Conciliation Bill carried into law.' And for once she was not only speaking for the WSPU.

June 1911 saw the return of Marguerite Norma-Smith, the Devon and Cornwall organiser for the NUWSS. In the eight years since Emmeline Pankhurst had broken from their ranks, the organisation had continued to lobby in their own way. Emmeline and Christabel still derided their tactics as ineffective, but the NUWSS was experiencing a surge in membership as more and more women walked away from the WSPU horrified by increasing militancy.

North Devon had remained virgin territory until Marguerite made her presence felt at the recent by-election. Capitalising on the interest generated then, and responses to a plea she'd made through the *North Devon Journal* for sympathisers, she decided it was time to start recruiting: 'I am delighted to be able to report the formation of four new societies in North Devon. The district was quite new ground when I came here some weeks ago. In Barnstaple Miss James [the same Kate James who spoke at the YMCA debate two years earlier and decried militancy at a later meeting] gave a small but successful meeting in her garden. Other members have been enrolled by visiting. The society at present is small (about 30 members) but we hope after a public meeting which we propose to have in the early autumn, the numbers will be considerably increased.' The report continued:

> At Instow, Mrs Preston-Whyte gave an afternoon meeting in her delightful drawing room. The meeting proved a great success and quite a number of people gave in their names as willing to join a local society. Since then Miss Preston-Whyte [the daughter] and I have collected more members and now Instow can boast a Suffrage Society of its own duly affiliated to the National Union.
>
> A quaint little fishing town of Appledore has yielded a surprising number of Suffragists. We have had two meetings in the church schools at both of which the vicar, the Rev G. Scholey has presided. Thanks to the energy and help Miss Martin has given, the Appledore Society now numbers some 51 members. Miss Martin has worked splendidly and I am delighted to leave the secretarial work of the society in her hands.
>
> On Tuesday of last week by kind permission of Miss Abbott, a meeting was held at West Bank School, Bideford, which has resulted in the formation of a Suffrage Society there … I am hoping to have another meeting in Bideford soon. As many people are asking to be told more about our movement. Four keen and enthusiastic societies in one constituency ought to make both political parties regard Women's Suffrage as a vital question.

While Ilfracombe had embraced militancy, it seemed the rest of the region was much more comfortable with the moderate approach of the NUWSS. But at the end of July both groups unusually found themselves working side-by-side. Under the heading 'Union is Strength', the NUWSS's mouthpiece, *The Common Cause*, announced: 'The news that the Women's Social and Political Union is going to work at all by-elections to support the candidate who will support the Conciliation Committee is the best news we have heard for a long time. It is a really statesmanlike resolve on the part of their leaders, and suffragists will feel themselves happy that now from end to end of the country their ranks are closed, their objects and methods are the same.'

It was a triumph of optimism over experience given Christabel Pankhurst's speech at a WSPU meeting just four months earlier when she made a characteristic rallying cry in favour of militant action. The NUWSS commented at the time: 'Unfortunately, far from emphasising the points of unity between all Suffragists, as Mrs Pankhurst had done, she [Christabel] denounced in vigorous terms those who chose to work by constitutional means, declaring that, in her opinion, they must, as women of intelligence, believe in militant action, and only abstained from taking part in it through cowardice.' Hardly a ringing endorsement of a united approach. But, for now at least, the two organisations shelved their differences as news came of another by-election, this time in West Somerset.

Both suffragists and suffragettes moved into the West Somerset constituency with a vengeance. Marguerite Norma-Smith coordinated her campaign from Taunton, where the candidates had their committee rooms, while Annie Kenney established her WSPU headquarters in Wellington. Annie immediately set to work organising meetings everywhere from Minehead to Dulverton, Porlock to Milverton. The choice to campaign against the Liberal was an easy one this time. Dudley Ward was committed to wrecking the Suffrage Bill, while the Conservative, Colonel Boles promised to do everything he could to get the Bill through. As always, the WSPU campaigned with military efficiency, drafting in speakers from across the country - and beyond. Their star speaker this time was Vida Goldstein, President of the Women's Political Association of Victoria, Australia.

It was a constant thorn in the side to the WSPU that while women in Australia had been able to vote since 1902, the UK government remained intransigent. Not only were Australians able to vote, but Vida Goldstein became the first woman in the British Empire to stand for election, albeit unsuccessfully, to a national parliament - inconceivable in Britain. Here was someone who could talk at first hand about the difference having the vote made. No more hypothesis, no more speculation, no more ill-founded prejudice. She countered wild assumptions, fears or notions with the facts and painted a vivid picture of how things were when women had the full support of their Prime Minister.

Andrew Fisher couldn't be more different from Asquith. He firmly believed that: 'no country could make real progress unless they took women in to their confidence and obtained their assistance through the exercise of the vote'. It was a belief reinforced by his wife. Both were in London in June 1911 - Prime Minister Fisher to attend the King's Coronation: Margaret Fisher to lead the Australian and New Zealand women in the Suffrage Procession.

All the familiar faces from the WSPU were out in force campaigning in West Somerset. Mrs Pankhurst was tireless, addressing crowds in Minehead, Taunton and Wellington, driven of course by her chauffeur, Vera Holme.

The *Western Morning News* was quick to comment. 'The crowd … showed some desire to catch a glimpse of the famous leader of the Suffragettes, and crowded round the motor car when it left the town [Wellington] … The Suffragists lose few opportunities to have a thrust at mere man. Even the chauffeur was a lady, and she certainly handled the car with considerable ease.'

Evelina Haverfield was also on the campaign trail, alongside Ann Martin, a former history professor at the University of Nevada. The good folks of rural Somerset must have struggled to understand these guest speakers, lurching between the antipodean twang of Vida Goldstein and the American drawl of Miss Martin.

It was an equal baptism of fire for Miss Martin: 'I have never before been to a country by-election and since I arrived in the motor car with Mrs Haverfield and Vera Holme last Monday have been living in a sort of whirlwind of political activity with Annie Kenney as its centre and driving force. Tuesday morning, a drive of four miles to Blagdon. House to house announcing an open air meeting at 8pm on the green. Drive back to chair an afternoon meeting at Wellington Town Hall. Back to Blagdon in the evening where women gather and listen with absorption and even self-forgetfulness on their toil-hardened faces as this working girl [Annie] who roused London and knew heavy labour as a child of ten tells her story of the rights and wrongs of women.'

Their gruelling schedule of open-air meetings often meant speaking at a crossroads in the middle of nowhere with an audience of farm workers and a few cattle. But they would still deliver a full-blown speech. And Annie proved herself over and over again. At Dulverton, where she addressed a crowd of over 400, a man was heard to remark, 'Jove she can talk! If only we had a few like her in Parliament instead of the muddlers we send there now!'

Marie Newby was there to support Annie. It was challenging at times, particularly when they addressed a crowd on the Esplanade at Watchet, yards away from a rival rally supporting the Liberal candidate. The paper reported: 'After a few words of introduction from Miss Kenney's companion, Mrs Newby, Miss Kenny commenced her address. She rapidly sketched the history of the agitation for the extension of the franchise … [she] had proceeded without much criticism, the crowd listening to her being comparatively thin, but with the termination of the Liberal meeting … the audience began to gather in strength and opposition. Miss Kenney preserved her sang-froid, in spite of persistent interruptions, and challenged her hecklers to put questions to her.' But the last thing the Liberal supporters were interested in was reasoned debate. They continued jeering and chanting until a riot threatened. Fortunately PC Penny, Watchet's village Bobby, bravely escorted Marie and Annie to safety.

The women claimed victory when the Conservative held the seat with a majority of 604. Their success was acclaimed in *Votes for Women,* alongside an advertisement featuring none other than Evelina Haverfield. She is depicted giving a ringing endorsement for the "Omne Tempus' Raincoat, the ideal coat, or so the advert goes, for Town, Country or Campaigning.

Chapter Ten
Tragedy in Ilfracombe
Late Summer 1911

While Marie was away, Anne Ball concentrated on the holiday campaign in Ilfracombe, as reported in *Votes for Women*. 'Much praise is due to Miss Ball who, whilst the secretary was away at the West Somerset by-election, arranged a daily WSPU stall in the Ilfracombe market. It has been a great success; many people coming and having a talk on Votes for Women. The market women also showing a keen interest. Miss Ball will take the stall at the market every Saturday during the season.'

Ilfracombe was inundated with visitors each summer and Anne Ball set her sights on converting them all. She put an advert in the paper inviting visitors to the stall where they sold 'Votes for Women' tea as well as the newsletter. It was a way to draw women in, get them talking and encourage them to a meeting. Meanwhile, someone who was becoming a core member of the group, Miss

Simes, was out and about on the streets selling the newsletter, with great success.

A lighter moment in the suffragettes' calendar was the annual Bideford carnival. On September 6th, Mrs Nash, a member of the WSPU and another enthusiastic seller of *Votes for Women,* won second prize for the best decorated bicycle. It was a triumphant incursion into the increasingly NUWSS dominated west of the region by Mrs Nash. Two years later, the South Devon resort of Seaton also saw a Suffrage Tableaux in their carnival, but on a very different theme. Entitled 'Forcible Feeding', participants posing as a doctor, warder, nurse and two suffragettes re-created the shocking scene.

Another person passionate about women's rights was a recent arrival in Ilfracombe, Cerisa Palmer. Although often distant and on edge, she was not afraid to take an unpopular stand in support of her beliefs. The previous year she had actively supported Charles Dolan, a Sinn Féin candidate, in the Irish elections. She was pelted with rotten eggs for her trouble, enough to drive her away, but it was an echo of a younger, fiery campaigner, single-minded in her pursuit of justice, now obscured by middle-aged jaundice.

But in the summer of 1911 there were signs that something was wrong. Cerisa became obsessed with news from Ireland that activist Helena Maloney had been arrested for throwing a stone through a pro-British shop window on Grafton Street, Dublin during the King's visit. When Maloney refused to pay the fine she was sentenced to a month in prison, becoming the first female jailed in the cause of Irish freedom since the days of the Ladies' Land League three decades earlier. Cerisa only calmed down when Maloney was released after her fine was paid anonymously.

Four weeks later Cerisa Palmer was dead.

'It was at the tunnels yesterday.' Marie breaks the silence. 'She was warned about the conditions. But she was used to them. She once told me she swam right across a bay in Ireland to get to an island. And she swam off the Tunnels beach nearly every day in all conditions. She liked to go in when the tide was coming in over the pool.'

All other business was forgotten as the women took in the tragic news. 'I've seen her,' Anne says. 'She was a bit eccentric, used to wear this strange bathing costume and make a complete circuit of the pool scrambling over the rocks, constantly shading her eyes with her hand before getting in the water. It wasn't something you missed. The holidaymakers would point and titter. So cruel.'

They nod, aware that the woman they'd embraced was often a talking point in the town. 'Apparently Mrs Rowe, her landlady, told her it was no kind of day to go bathing,' Marie continued, 'but typically all she got from Cerisa was "rubbish". Mr Austin, the attendant, saw her arrive. He pointed out the heavy sea running outside the wall but she didn't seem concerned. It was peculiar though. Apparently she begged a girl not to go in because the water was dangerous. If she was anxious for the girl, why not for herself?'

'It doesn't make sense.'

There were no answers. Just questions. 'Mr Austin said it wasn't long before she drifted out over the wall and got into trouble. He tried to reach her with a pole but couldn't, so he ran for PC Bedford and they launched a boat. She was still swimming then but the sea was rough and they were beaten back. The third time of trying they reached her about twenty yards from the shore. She was floating on her back gasping for breath, but alive.

'When Mr Austin and PC Bedford got her onto the beach the doctor was waiting. He thought he felt a pulse so they moved her to the Baths where he asked for hot water bottles. But it was no good. She'd gone.'

It was only later that the truth emerged. The lady the group thought they knew was not Cerisa Palmer … but Anna Catherine Parnell, a legend in Irish history.

Immediately the questions started. Why adopt an alias? Why leave her home, her country, her life to live as a stranger in Ilfracombe? Was there something in her past dark enough to pursue her across the Channel to this town, to this beach? Maybe it was more than a few eggs she was threatened with for her support of Sinn Féin.

Suddenly it all made sense. Ireland, her politics, her passion - even the writing. Her book was called the *Tale of a Great Sham,* an account of the Ladies' Land League, the organisation Anna Parnell founded and led at the end of the nineteenth century to fight for tenants' rights. She'd travelled all over Ireland as a young woman, speaking, protesting, standing up to bailiffs and police at evictions. The Ladies' Land League pitched itself against the Liberal Government but in the end it was her own brother, Charles Parnell, leading light of the Irish Home Rule movement, who brought it to an end. Anna refused to go along with the deal he set up with Gladstone and his government, a deal with the very leaders she'd denounced. Unthinkable! It was the ultimate treachery. Anna cut off all ties with her brother and fled to England, only returning occasionally to link up with Helena Moloney or campaign for Sinn Féin.

Once the truth was out it explained a great deal, particularly her agitation over Helena Moloney. Anna wrote *The Tale of a Great Sham* in 1907 and entrusted it to Helena, editor of the nationalist women's paper *Bean na h-Eireann*, to publish. Convinced it would never happen with Helena in gaol, she paid her fine anonymously.

The papers reported a tragic accident. But some in Ilfracombe wondered if there was more to it. According to one eye witness there was no cry for help when she got into trouble in the water. Not a sound, perhaps because she was swamped by a wave or thrown against a rock and knocked unconscious. But witnesses reported she was conscious, maybe intent on allowing events to take their course?

The mystery over Anna Catherine Parnell's life and death remains. Even in her lifetime she was an enigma. Katherine Tynan, writing in *Twenty-five years: Reminiscences* describes her as: 'the

stuff of which heroines are made, perhaps she alone of us. And what soft, gentle stuff it was! ... One would have said she was masculine if she had not been so feminine. The small pale face, strangely attractive, was very sensitive, somewhat nervous.'

Before her self-imposed exile, Anna had been a vital part of the political landscape in Ireland and intimately connected to two others who shared her feisty approach to politics. The first was Jennie Wyse Power, co-founder of 'Daughters of Ireland', an active member of Dublin's Women's Suffrage Association and, by the time of Anna's death, inextricably linked with Sinn Féin. Three years later she was elected the first President of Cumann na mBan, an Irish republican women's paramilitary organisation. Soon after, she was succeeded as President by the next woman in this chain of close friendships, and someone who was to make electoral history in 1918, the Countess Markievicz.

When she died in 1911, Anna Catherine Parnell was just fifty-nine. Her funeral was a muted affair with none of her family present. Her two sisters and a brother left everything to her landlady Mrs Rowe to arrange. The only mourners were Mrs Rowe and sister, and Mr Parkin, Mr Austin and Mr Knill from the Tunnels Beaches. But Cerisa Palmer reclaimed her true identity in death. The coffin that was lowered into the grave bore the inscription *Catherine A Parnell.*

It was time for other farewells in Ilfracombe, some brief, some more final. The group had lost Evelina after the summer break, she was now back in London busy chairing the Paddington branch of the WSPU. More of a blow was the news that Annie Kenney was returning to her roots, organising a special campaign for the pit-brow women in Wigan. True, the Ilfracombe and Barnstaple branch was forging ahead with its own momentum while other places were desperately in need of Annie's passion, but she would be sorely missed. Fittingly she left as she'd arrived, with a plea that the group get sewing for an upcoming Fair: 'I am most anxious that the West of England stall should look the very best, have the largest stock, take the most money. I recommend weekly sewing meetings, visits to shops to ask if they'll help by giving linens, silk or cotton to make bags with. Each member should visit her dressmaker and milliner and ask for remnants.'

The group responded: 'The secretary has had promises of help for the Bag and Basket Stall. Will others also make at least one bag or send a contribution to her? Members please attend the work party. Wed. Oct. 25 St Mary's Broad Park Ave. 3pm,' It was to be the first of their weekly sewing work parties. It was tame stuff compared with the momentum they'd built up through the spring and summer but their biggest challenge through the autumn of 1911 was to be patience.

Asquith eventually caved in, or so it seemed, to outrage over the wrecking tactics announced by Lloyd George with an assurance that the Suffrage Bill would be progressed: 'I have no hesitation in saying that the promises made by, and of behalf of, the Government in regard to giving facilities for the Conciliation Bill will be strictly adhered to both in letter and in spirit.'

But not yet. Not even this year, but next.

Amazingly Christabel took him at his word, astonishing given his track record, and responded with the offer of a continued truce over militancy: 'The women's movement for political emancipation has gone through testing times. Physical violence, ridicule, abuse, persecution, imprisonment, torture. Now the movement is undergoing the hardest test of all - the test of peace and postponement, the test of a long truce from militant action in return for a definite pledge of facilities next year for the Conciliation Bill.'

Evelina was sceptical. *The Bath Chronicle and Weekly Gazette* reported her speech to the Bath WSPU: 'After remarking that women were capable of making any sacrifices for love of their country, Mrs

Haverfield condemned the doctrine of patience and supported that of impatience and concluded by expressing a hope that next year would see the success of all their efforts.'

It was a hope Barnstaple MP, Sir Geoffrey Baring, played with at the AGM of the Barnstaple Women's Association. On the one hand he was keen to stress that to give lip service to women's suffrage then do the utmost to delay further progress simply 'wasn't cricket.' But, jumping on Lloyd George's bandwagon, he then stated he would not support any Bill giving a limited franchise to women. He looked forward to the time when every man and woman of twenty-one and not a lunatic or criminal would have the vote.

The Government's plan was on a roll and about to sink the best chance women had ever had to claim the vote.

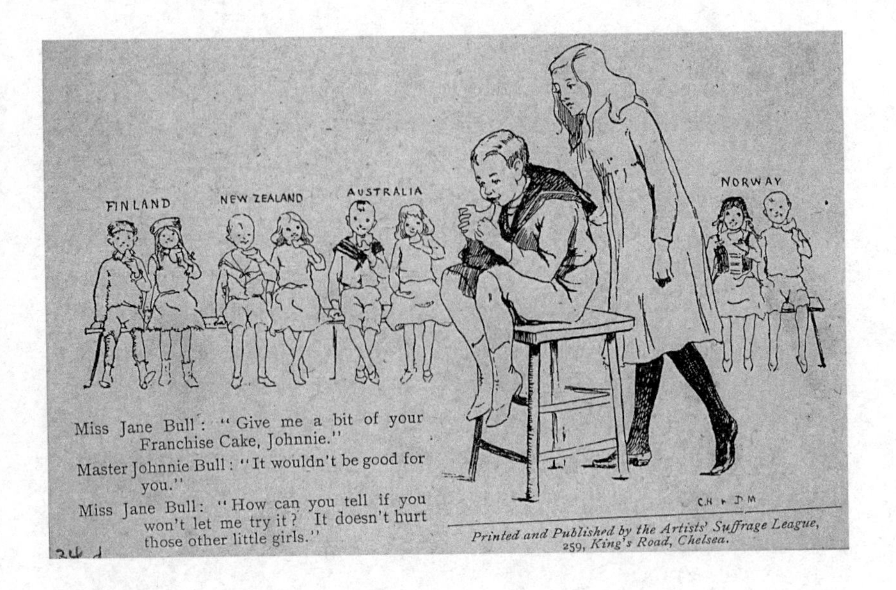

Chapter Eleven
Devon Swells the London Protest
Autumn, 1911

On November 10th, the Ilfracombe group gathered for a working party when *Votes for Women* broke the news: 'On Tuesday last the Prime Minister made the announcement that it is the intention of the Government to introduce a Franchise Bill next session ... [This Bill] will be confined to adult males; women will be excluded.'

Women will be excluded!

Asquith had made a public commitment to proceed with the Suffrage Bill. He had promised. Despite so many past betrayals he had been believed. Not any more. Now every woman in the country could see that his word was worthless. The article continued. 'From this announcement it will be seen that the Government have decided to range themselves definitely in opposition to Woman Suffrage. In spite of the fact that there is an agitation for giving votes to women which is national in its scope and unprecedented in its magnitude ... the Government are proposing to give more votes to men and none to women. In consequence of this attitude, the Women's Social and Political Union have decided to resume immediately their militant anti-Government policy.'

The press was uncharacteristically sympathetic:

> We are no friends of female suffrage, but anything more contemptible than the attitude assumed by the Government, it is difficult to imagine. *The Globe*.
>
> Any male, however regardless of his civic duties, is to be endowed, without effort on his part, with the right to govern his fellow citizens; no female - if Mr Asquith has his way - is to have any share in the government of her country, however great her capacity, however large her contributions to the public revenue. *The Daily Graphic*.
>
> For our part, if there were to be any question of Adult Suffrage we should oppose to the last any partial measure which excluded thousands of educated and responsible women from the Suffrage while opening the gates of political power to mobs of utterly ignorant men. *The Daily Express*.
>
> The advocates of Women's Suffrage will, of course, be furious. Mr Asquith's bombshell will blow the Conciliation Bill to smithereens. *The Evening News*.
>
> The Government have certainly dealt a deadly blow at the Women's Suffrage movement in Parliament. *The Yorkshire Post*.
>
> WAR IS DECLARED - DECLARED BY THE GOVERNMENT UPON WOMEN. *Votes for Women*.

The WSPU responded immediately, announcing a deputation to Westminster to demand that the proposed Manhood Suffrage Bill be abandoned. They intended to confront the Prime Minister and the person they now considered just as much the architect of their downfall - Lloyd George: 'It is an open secret that the whole idea of the introduction by the Government in 1912 of a Manhood Suffrage Bill emanated from the brain of Mr Lloyd George, who has for a long time been scheming to wreck the Conciliation Bill. Baffled in other attempts at mischief, the Chancellor of the Exchequer has devised this latest scheme of destruction, which he trusts will effectively achieve his end.'

Asquith's duplicity was predictable. His next move was not. A letter arrived at WSPU headquarters addressed to Mrs Pethick-Lawrence: 'Dear Madam - I am desired by the Prime Minister ... to inform you that arrangements have already been made for the Prime Minister to receive a deputation from various suffrage societies at 11.30 on Friday, November 17th at 10 Downing Street, including your own society if you desire it ... The Chancellor of the Exchequer will be present with the Prime Minister.'

After years of refusing to admit any deputations, years that resulted in the brutal treatment and imprisonment of hundreds of women, the WSPU was finally being invited inside the doors of Downing Street. They immediately began formulating their demands. The Conciliation Bill was dead. It was time to regroup. They had always campaigned for the vote on the same terms as men. If men were now to have the franchise on an unlimited basis then they would accept nothing less than an unlimited franchise for women. It was a knee-jerk reaction that was to have profound consequences.

On a damp November morning, representatives from the WSPU, the NUWSS, the Women's Freedom League and other suffrage societies made their way to Downing Street for the meeting with Asquith and Lloyd George. It was the face-to-face dialogue that both suffragists and suffragettes had long demanded. Asquith was quick to take control of the situation. He reassured the Ladies that a private members' amendment could be made to The Reform Bill to extend the franchise to women and, despite his personal belief that this would not benefit the state, his government would respect the view of Parliament on this.

The ladies from the NUWSS were content to take him at his word. The WSPU were not. They knew that no private members' amendment would gain a majority. It was a trick, another tactic to sabotage their efforts. They left the meeting determined that the militant campaign would go forward with more vigour than ever, spurred on by Christabel's rallying cry:

> Some people, and of them the WSPU is made, do not shrink from their mission ... They do not fight with their own strength, they do not speak with their own voice, they are the instruments of a Power greater than themselves. Ours is a great crusade. We ask you all to join us. March under our banner. Share the victory that is before us.

Marie closes the door to the sitting room and settles herself in her favourite chair. She folds back the pages of 'Votes for Women' to reveal a piece by Christabel. 'A Call to Arms,' the headline announces. 'On Tuesday next at 7.30pm Caxton Hall will be crowded with women who will assemble for the purpose of resolving upon such action, whether militant or otherwise, as the Prime Minister's statement of to-day may render necessary. It will be an historic gathering, perhaps the most important since the movement began. Names are coming in steadily for the deputation to the Prime Minster (should this be necessary) - volunteers should write at once to Miss Christabel Pankhurst... You want the deputation to go; you want the protest to be made; you don't want this Bill destroyed, but how can you expect other women to do anything if you do nothing yourselves? Who are you that you are privileged to stand aside and clap your hands at the sacrifices that other are making? Why is it more difficult for you to join this deputation than it is for others? ***It is most important that all those who are prepared to take action if action be required should write without delay to Clements Inn.'***

Marie sighs. Halls in London overflow with women cheering and applauding Mrs Pankhurst and Christabel's call to arms while she sits here in her comfortable armchair. Even Mr Pethick-Lawrence, whom she so admired when he came to Ilfracombe, stated such treachery can only be met with action. She reads on. 'I know all the things people say to prevent your going. They will say you cannot go because you are too much missed in your home; you are too much wanted outside Holloway Gaol. Well, you would not be worth very much if you were not wanted, whatever your circle of activities and energies happen to be! It is because of that that you ought to be on this deputation. It is not idle women, but thinking women who should be there … every woman who feels like that should be go with us on that deputation on Tuesday.'

Marie's hands tremble. How can she restrict her activities to the streets of Ilfracombe and leave other women to carry this burden? It is time to fully embrace the WSPU slogan - Deeds not Words. But if Asquith refuses to give the answer they want, as Marie knows in her heart will be the case, then she will face violence, arrest… and prison.

Holloway. Simply a word to her now but soon to become all too real.

A few days later Marie steps onto the platform at Paddington station. She nods farewell to her fellow travellers, picks her way through the bustling atrium and emerges onto the London streets. At first the crowd is mixed but the closer she draws to Caxton Hall, the more women surround her. At the door she is handed a typewritten sheet giving a list of instructions about what to do when she is arrested - not if, when. She is to refuse to go to her cell, refuse to undress, refuse to be medically examined, refuse to scrub out.

It's a brutal wake-up call, this piece of paper telling her she will be put in solitary confinement in punishment cells. Her reality in a few short hours? Yet all around women are chatting and laughing, carried along on a wave of subdued excitement. They are on the verge of making history. The future of women across the country, the world even, depends on what they do next.

She moves forward as the stewards check her name and direct her to seats reserved for volunteers for the deputation. Somewhere in the crowd is Evelina, an old hand at these demonstrations. She will make sure she is arrested, given her moment in court and sent to Holloway. The experienced protestors are easy to spot, they are the ones padded with cotton wool and cardboard to protect their ribs from the blows. But this is Marie's first time. There will be no shame in taking things step-by-step.

The hall bursts into life as Mrs Pankhurst, Christabel and others take the stage. Handkerchiefs and flags are waved and cries of 'Bravo' ring out. It's a defining moment, the first time Marie has seen Emmeline and Christabel in the flesh. Suddenly she understands. Perhaps it's the noise, the charged atmosphere or the crush, but even at this distance their charisma is magnetic.

Mrs Pankhurst raises her hand to speak. 'The Government's pronouncement is a trap which we decline to enter. I move the following resolution. This meeting condemns the Government's announcement of a Manhood Suffrage Bill as a grave and unpardonable insult to women; (Cheers) firmly refuses to allow the political enfranchisement of women to depend upon a mere amendment to the Manhood Suffrage Bill; (Cheers) demands that the Government abandons the Manhood Suffrage Bill and introduce and carry in the next Session of Parliament a measure giving precisely equal franchise rights to men and women. (Cheers) And further, the meeting declares its resolve to enforce this reasonable demand upon the attention of the Government and of the electors by vigorous and determined militant action.' (Cheers and applause)

Mrs Pethick-Lawrence steps forward. She has been alongside Emmeline Pankhurst since the earliest days of the WSPU. She and her husband, Frederick, publish 'Votes for Women' and, together, contribute thousands to the campaign fund. She also knows what it is like to experience the degradation of Holloway. 'The objective of the deputation,' she opens, 'is to protest on the floor of the House of Commons, in the presence of all the members, against the deep insult of manhood suffrage that has been offered to the womanhood of the country. Nothing will make us turn our backs except, of course, physical force.

'But we who are on the deputation tonight are already outside our body. We know that our hands, our feet, and all that we have are being used by the great Spirit to carry out the great purpose of His will. It is that which destroys any possibility of anxiety or fear or consciousness of pain. We know that here we offer and present ourselves, our souls and bodies, to be a living sacrifice for all those great sins of the world whose taproot is in sex discrimination. We go tonight not only to fight for the freedom of the women of our own country, but to carry a message of deliverance to the whole world.'

Marie knows the sustaining force of her religion, but to hear the words used like this ... she is simultaneously fired with zeal and shot through with apprehension. But there's no time for indecision. The speeches are over and she is swept out of the Hall, a small particle in an unstoppable mass. No more than a few yards on they are confronted by a cordon of police. A struggle begins at once until, suddenly, the cordon breaks and the leaders are let through. It closes again almost immediately but then another small group are let through. It's soon clear. The police are briefed to break the demonstration up into small parties, thwarting their intention to become a procession. Marie follows when her turn comes. As she reaches the corner of Parliament Square she sees women caught up in the fiercest struggles. Even the small groups are broken by the surging crowd and the mounted policemen. In the melee she recognises Vera Holme seizing a horse's bridle and trying to turn it around, fearless of the mounted policeman's attempts to beat her away.

Women hurl themselves at the police cordon surrounding the House of Commons but again and again they are forced back into the crowd or manhandled away under arrest. Marie finds herself separated and set upon in the crush. Her hair is grabbed, and she is dragged along the road, her head pulled back until her eyes water. She makes herself a dead weight until, suddenly, she is released. She drops to the ground, curling up to prevent being trampled.

Unknown hands half-support, half-carry her, barely conscious, free of the crowd. The relief is overwhelming. She'd felt threatened by the rowdy Liberal supporters in Watchet but that was nothing compared to this. She watches from the sidelines. Her protest is over … for now.

Many of the 220 women arrested that day had been alongside Marie Newby in Parliament Square. Others took part in a frenzied bout of window-smashing of Government offices, the Liberal Club and shopfronts along the Strand. According to *The Morning Advertiser* there was only one conclusion to be drawn: 'There are only two possible courses. Either the claims of the women must be conceded or the disorder which their agitation causes must be put down by force. It may even be necessary to resort to corporal punishment.'

Chapter Twelve
The Voice of Militancy
Winter of 1911

The mood in Ilfracombe was sombre. Marie had escaped imprisonment but many familiar names hadn't. Evelina Haverfield, sentenced to fourteen days, Vera Holme, six days, and worst of all, Vera Wentworth, six months. And there was another name the group recognised, Olive Wharry from Holsworthy - someone Marie was to get to know very much better in a few months' time.

Lady Constance Lytton put up a fighting defence. When brought before the court accused of using a hammer and stones to break windows she said: 'It is the only effective form of protest left to us by a Government which boasts of Liberalism and representation where men are concerned but ignores the elementary principle of representation where women are concerned. Votes and riot are the only form of appeal to which the Government will respond. They refuse us votes; therefore we fall back on riot. The wrongs they inflict on women are intolerable and we will no longer tolerate them.'

Jessie Smith, someone the group was soon to meet, was singled out. A veteran of five court appearances, she was charged with breaking a pane of glass at the Treasury. In her defence she said she was a tax-paying woman and had tried by peaceful propaganda to work for the emancipation of her sex, but after Mr Asquith's last proposal she threw the stone where she thought she ought to have some entrance, into the Treasury window.

This outburst of WSPU militancy reverberated around the country, creating a backlash. Miss Davenport, the new organiser for the South Western Federation of the NUWSS, decided it was the perfect moment to step up recruitment in North Devon. Meetings were going well in Bideford. At the last, held at Miss Doolette's Cutround Tea Rooms, their speaker, Mrs Mayer, held the attention of a packed room with an account of the Women's Suffrage Movement in Australia.

Miss Davenport's next target was Barnstaple. An advert appeared on the front page of the North Devon Journal, emphasising the non-party, non-militant stance of the organisation. She invited all sympathisers to get in touch with her at 2 Park Villas with a view to forming a Barnstaple branch of the NUWSS. Her appeal was so successful an inaugural meeting was held in the parish rooms the following week. There was only one possible focus for Miss Davenport's address - the positive non-militant alternative the NUWSS provided to the WSPU. Her message was embraced with enthusiasm. The Barnstaple and District Suffrage Society was born with Mrs Morgan as Hon. Secretary, Miss Harston treasurer, and

Mesdames Reavell, Knill and Hutchings, and Misses James, Adams, Goss, Hunt, Johnstone and Cousins forming the committee alongside nine other members.

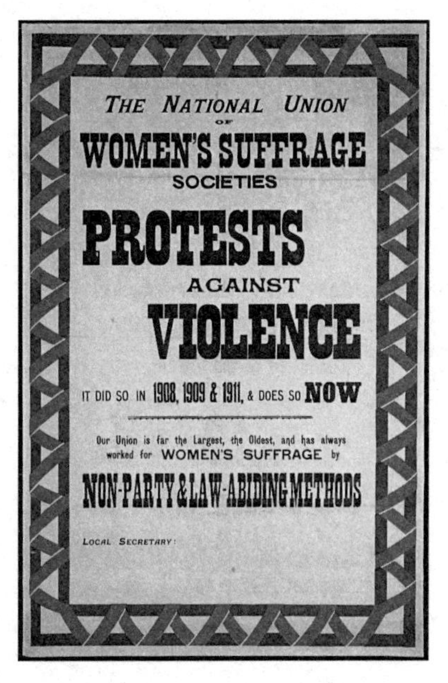

The WSPU had to counter this backlash driving women towards the NUWSS. *Votes for Women* had the answer: 'There is nothing at the moment so important from the political point of view as increasing the circulation of the paper. Even those who believe in a vague and general way that women ought to have the vote jump to the conclusion that though we have been right in our militant methods in the past, we are wrong in the very last and latest development. For are not all the daily papers, whether Conservative or Liberal, saying so? And what everybody agrees in saying must of course be sound sense! The only people who do not get bamboozled in this way are the regular readers of VOTES FOR WOMEN. There they see dangers foreshadowed before they arrive; they see by which way alone those dangers can be met and overcome. They are prepared beforehand for every new development of the struggle and are made aware of every new necessity of action.'

Ilfracombe soon had the perfect opportunity to promote the paper. A meeting had been arranged at the Gaiety Hall for WSPU members and the general public to hear someone who had been active in Devon longer than anyone else, Mrs Montague, Hon. Secretary of the Exeter branch. Appearing alongside her was to be Miss Jessie Smith - someone well able to bring the horror of Holloway to this sleepy Devon town.

On a dark Monday evening, Marie escorts May Montague and Jessie Smith to the Gaiety Hall. She is buoyed up by the work she and Jessie have done over the past week. Jessie has sold over a hundred copies of 'Votes for Women' in the shops and on the streets, engaging so many women in conversation. It's an invaluable opportunity for Marie to listen and learn, seeing how women warm to Jessie's passion and conviction. No more hiding in the shadows. She will be a passionate advocate for the cause, claiming a prominent vantage point in town by the market arch to sell 'Votes for Women'. To make sure she is seen, she will wear the bold apron Sylvia has designed to advertise the magazine. Emmeline Pethick-Lawrence is right. The only people not bamboozled by the mainstream press are the regular readers, as Jessie had reminded the Ilfracombe members a few days earlier.

Now a much bigger crowd is pouring into this sea-side theatre, set in a terrace of shops and cafes opposite the magnificent glass house on Ilfracombe's promenade. It has only been open just over a year but is already a popular choice for variety shows. Its modest entrance through one of the shops belies the scale of the auditorium at first floor level. Capable of holding 650, it is

almost at capacity as Mrs Montague opens the meeting. Her message is clear: 'Women are denied the rights and privileges of citizens simply because they are women … when women get the vote they will use it to better their conditions, just as men did, and to get their grievances redressed, which is impossible as long as they are not enfranchised. Mr Asquith has said that the only opinion he considers is the vote at the poll. Women wanted the vote in order to express their opinion there. While with the vote, men who were supposed to be the stronger sex, were armed with a weapon with which to defend themselves, women were unarmed. Slavery had been defined as government without the consent of the governed, therefore women who were governed without their own consent were really slaves.'

It is fighting talk. She moves on to the increasingly complicated issue of the Suffrage Bill: 'The government is going to introduce a Manhood Suffrage Bill without including women. Yes, it is open to any amendment but this will not get enough votes. It will be defeated. The Suffragists demand that votes for women be made part of the Government Bill.' It is a clear statement of intent that those in the hall are easily able to grasp.

Jessie is next to speak; her mission - to arouse the audience's sympathies: 'Yes, I am a militant suffragist. But history would never have been written but for the successful fights for justice and for people rising against bad laws and making good laws instead. There are women in the industrial markets living under conditions no better than slavery. Women's influence is needed in politics for they understand some social evils better than men.

'Militant methods have been described as disgraceful and unwomanly, but it is more unwomanly and disgraceful to tolerate the conditions of life under which women suffer. A number of MPs signed a petition protesting against the recent conduct of the suffragettes but they did not protest against the damage done by the Carnarvonshire strikers last July - simply because they had votes and women did not.'

Jessie Smith's mention of 'a number of MPs' is an understatement. Over a hundred MPs condemned the actions of the WSPU, convinced that their conduct made the organisation of an effective campaign in favour of women's suffrage difficult, if not impossible. Even Ramsay MacDonald, Leader of the Labour party, was uncompromising: 'One would prefer to be oblivious to, and to forget, the degrading and disgusting scenes at which we have just been looking. Those of us who have any regard for womanhood those of us who have any ideals, regarding woman's intelligence and woman's conduct must simply bow their head in shame. If I felt the cause had come to this I would go into the lobby every time against it.' On this December evening, Jessie Smith is in the firing line from those in agreement with Ramsay MacDonald.

'Do you not think,' a questioner asks, 'that in bringing about meetings of this kind you would do more to further your cause than by breaking windows and damaging the facial appearance of ministers?'

'We have tried to arouse public opinion by meetings,' Jessie replies, 'but that in itself has failed. So we have followed the example of the men when they were agitating for the vote. But we do not go so far for the men attacked individuals and burned houses.'

'Are the majority of the members of the Women's Social and Political Union in favour of militant methods?'

'They are all in favour.' Jessie seeks out a familiar face in the audience. 'Ilfracombe was represented in the person of Mrs Newby at the last demonstration and I hope the next time Mrs Newby will take honours by graduating in the suffragette university at Holloway.'

It was a very public challenge for Marie.

Only a few days earlier at the Braunton Liberal Club, Mr Smith, of Barnstaple, had quoted Asquith: 'If female suffrage became law it would be an unknown, unmeasured disaster and a calamity to the nation.' A view shared by his cabinet minister, William Harcourt. 'I believe that for women to become part of the political machine is bad for themselves and bad for the country. I think that it draws them from the spheres in which they shine, from duties which they adorn, from duties which can adequately be performed by none but themselves. Women of course possess emotion and charm. These are great assets, but I do not think they are conducive to sober political judgement. Then there are physical and physiological circumstances in their lives which are more fitted for discussion in the consulting room than on the platform, circumstances which unfit them for public duty or judgement.'

Enough to raise hackles then and now. But militancy was still a controversial choice. It had found a home in Ilfracombe but elsewhere in North Devon, women continued to be drawn to the more moderate approach of the NUWSS. In early 1912 a second meeting of the newly formed Barnstaple branch, held at Pilton Glove works, attracted a large audience of female workers. And at a subsequent meeting, Dr Mary Morris, briefly returning to her old stamping ground as a former house surgeon at the North Devon Infirmary, proposed that: 'this society disagrees altogether with the tactics of the militant Suffragettes.'

The Appledore group was also thriving: 'A most enthusiastic meeting was held on January 11th when Miss Willcocks (Exeter) spoke on "Why Women Want the Vote" and Miss Davenport on the political situation. The hall was brightly decorated with posters and the colours and the meeting roused great enthusiasm, one old inhabitant offering the speaker "her heart's blood". The wives of sailors and fishermen are determined to help to get the vote. The one difficulty in this branch is the extreme poverty of the township. The largest subscription received is five and a half pence.'

Miss Davenport spoke at several meetings throughout January 1912. With the support of Miss Gibbings, of Northam, she moved easily between an afternoon appearance at the Bideford Women's Liberal Association and a cottage meeting at Northam in the evening. Then it was on to Instow, and a gathering organised by Miss Joanna Preston-Whyte, before returning to the regular Bideford venue, the Cut Round Tea Rooms, and rounding off her North Devon tour in style with a social hosted by Appledore on January 25th.

Undeterred, the WSPU were also getting their message across with new members swelling the weekly meetings at Ilfracombe. Miss Warren, Mrs Dovell, Mrs Mumford, Mrs Turiss, Miss Bendle, Miss Wormall, Miss Bull, Miss Heselton and many more gathered to hear some good news. The Labour Party had carried a resolution that: 'This Conference, in harmony with previous decisions, is of the opinion that the enfranchisement of all adult men and women should be included in the Reform Bill to be introduced by the Government in the coming Session of Parliament. It further requests the Labour Party in Parliament to make it clear that no Bill can be acceptable to the Labour and Socialist movement which does not include women.'

Over Christmas the group was boosted by the arrival of Evelina at Brendon. It was the perfect place for her to recuperate from a recent incarceration in Holloway, filling her days with gentle walks by the East Lynn and long rides across the moor. There was also time to catch up with Marie, Anne and all the new faces in Ilfracombe. Coming so close to Jessie's visit, Evelina's account of her experiences in Holloway may well have been too close for comfort for some. Particularly Marie. What was the point in being part of the protest and simply returning home? Getting arrested, refusing to pay the fines, being imprisoned was the whole point. Evelina hadn't shirked her duty.

By the New Year, Evelina was back in London, more determined that ever to make good on her words to Sir Albert de Rutzen from the dock at Bow Street Court: 'May I say that my whole attitude is a protest against the way the police were instructed to treat our women on Friday. It was the most monstrous thing I have ever known, and when I say I will take a revolver I mean that I will carry on this agitation when I come out of prison with more vigour than ever. We shall carry our point, sir, with all respect to you I am bound to make my protest.'

In one week alone she had three speaking engagements - Monday to a large audience at Kensington; Tuesday at Wimbledon; Wednesday at Streatham. And she had been so successful as Chair of the Paddington branch of the WSPU that they were forced to take on larger premises, celebrating their opening with a musical evening including a performance by Vera Holme.

The Ilfracombe group also indulged in more light-hearted evenings from time to time. 'A most enjoyable evening was spent by the members who accepted Miss Ball's kind invitation for Shrove Tuesday. Prizes were given for the different games and impromptu speeches were made.' It was welcome light relief from the notice received by Anne Ball that her goods would again be seized and sold at auction, the now predictable reaction to her refusal to pay her taxes.

It was an effective public protest but Marie was haunted by Jessie's words: 'I hope the next time Mrs Newby will take honours by graduating in the suffragette university at Holloway.' It was a call to action she could no longer ignore.

Marie paces the carpet, Emmeline Pethick-Lawrence's words ringing in her ears: 'We are intellectually convinced that unless we can make trouble for the Government we must remain in the political subjection which penalises women in every aspect and avocation of their life and heaps misery upon the wretched and degradation upon the wronged. This intellectual conviction, united with the strong moral compulsion that has welded us together in this Movement, obliges every woman in our ranks to take her place in the demonstration of protests that will be made on Monday, March 4 against the exclusion of women from the Government's programme of electoral reform.

'There is not a woman in the world who is not indispensable to some person … in her own circle. Not one but has had to leave husband or brother, sister or mother, who she loved better than herself, not one who has not caused grief in hearts intensely dear to her, not one who has not incurred disapproval, not one who has not linked the loss of friends to the withdrawal of affection. That is the price they have paid for a great ideal and for the deliverance of those too weak, too poor, or too rigidly held in bondage to help themselves.'

For Marie, March 4th 1912 must mark a turning point. Mrs Pankhurst was demanding that she stand up and be counted: 'I cannot say too often that the success of the next protest depends upon its size. We have courage and determination in this movement. What we lack is actual fighting members. Come if it is humanly possible for you to come! We cannot go into the conscience of every woman. We cannot weigh her reasons for and against coming with us. That is the responsibility upon each of us, but I can say, and my colleagues can say with me, that we believe the call now is so great that nothing but the most vital necessity should prevent women … from coming to take part in this protest. I believe from the bottom of my heart that if we are determined enough, if we are courageous enough, the enemy will be glad to bring this struggle of ours to a speedy close.'

Marie looked again at the letters from women who had already answered the call.

'Will you please put my name down for the protest on March 4. I have not joined in any of the other protests but feel it is my duty to do so.'

'Will you put my name down for the demonstration for the sake of the children…'

'Though I am almost an invalid, I have still strength enough to volunteer to throw a stone of protest and I cannot be a coward any longer … I am not at all heroic over physical suffering but if you will have my name I shall feel honoured to be permitted to swell your fighting ranks on March 4.'

'If only we could muster in our thousands and show this tyrannical so-called Liberal Government (whose methods of treating political prisoners are worthy of the middle-ages) that the just demands of the women of this country can no longer be ignored.'

No more hesitation. Marie sits at her desk, takes an envelope and addresses it to Miss Christabel Pankhurst, 4 Clements Inn, London, W.C. She will be standing side by side with these women on Monday, 4th March.

Within days Marie received a letter thanking her for rallying to the cause and informing her she would be given specific instructions when she arrived at Clements Inn on the day. The letter also contained a card of admittance to the Gardenia restaurant in Catherine Street and a stark slip of paper telling her she would be arrested, and that she should bring a change of clothes with her. She is to carry nothing. No umbrella, nothing. She may leave a portmanteau at Clements Inn and it will be transported to Bow Street for her appearance there.

So methodical, so matter of fact, so final. Marie has crossed an invisible line, now committed to actions that were inconceivable only a year before.

Mrs. Partington again: "WAIT, WAIT, WHY CAN'T YOU WAIT?"

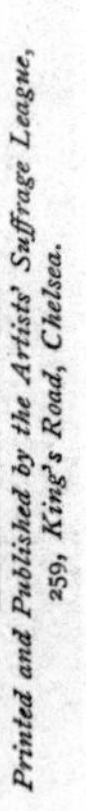
Printed and Published by the Artists' Suffrage League, 259, King's Road, Chelsea.

Chapter Thirteen
Graduating at Holloway
Spring 1912

They stand in silence at Ilfracombe station, waiting for the London Express. Marie draws her overcoat closer around her slim frame, wincing as the biting sea air sweeps across the platform. Her husband stands alongside, grasping her arm just a little tighter than necessary. How easy it would be to return to their homely villa in Broad Park Avenue. Easy, but not an option, not this time.

Marie checks her portmanteau. Cotton wool, newspaper, small stones, identification, a change of dress, the bare essentials. 'I've left menus with Annie,' she says, anxious to break the silence between them. 'You just need to give her your schedule each week. And Sarah will attend to any household matters.'

'I'll be perfectly well taken care of. I just wish I could say the same of you.' He squeezes her hand discreetly; his touch is reassuring. There's no turning back, Marie knows that, but shivers at the prospect of what lies ahead. It was one thing to witness the appalling brutality from the sidelines,

but this time she will be standing shoulder to shoulder with her sisters. No-one knows what will happen then, not even Mrs Pankhurst.

With a final wave, Marie boards the 7.30am express and settles herself into a compartment. There's an annoying wait of over an hour at Barnstaple for her connection but she arrives in London by 1.30pm, plenty of time to get to the briefing at Clements Inn. There she joins the growing queue of women. Hundreds have answered the call to make their voice heard. It is to be a protest the like of which London has never seen. They must never doubt their cause is just.

MEN AND WOMEN
I INVITE YOU TO
COME TO
PARLIAMENT SQUARE
ON
MONDAY, March 4, 1912,
at 8 o'clock,
TO TAKE PART IN A
GREAT PROTEST MEETING
against the Government's refusal to include women in their Reform Bill.

Speeches will be delivered by well-known Suffragettes, who want to enlist your sympathy and help in the great battle they are fighting for human liberty.

(Signed) E. PANKHURST.

They are ushered inside to where Mrs Pankhurst is waiting to speak: 'On arriving at Holloway you are to refuse to go to your cells until you have seen the governor. If forcibly taken, you must refuse to be medically examined. You are to protest at being held as common criminals and refuse to wear prison clothes. If, as is likely, you are forcibly undressed you must remain calm and polite with the warders. Your strongest weapon is passive resistance and endurance, whatever the cost. As a protest against insufficient air, you are to wait for a bell to ring at 1pm and then break a pane of glass with heel of your shoe.

'We shall most likely be in solitary confinement, in punishment cells, probably in separate prisons. But we will be together in spirit. Now, please ensure your portmanteaus are clearly labelled with your name and leave them in the hallway. You will be given a typewritten sheet as you leave telling you where to go. It is vital you each follow your instructions to be sure that you are all where you need to be when the time comes.'

Marie joins a group directed to a coffee shop to wait. She shuffles anxiously on her chair, convinced that every man who approaches is a plain clothes policeman intent on apprehending her. This time there will be no gentleman to carry her to safety. This time she will be arrested. She glances discreetly at her sheet. It's 3pm, time to move on to the Gardenia restaurant in Catherine Street.

Noise and warmth swamp her as she climbs the stairs to the second floor room where she is swallowed up in a mass of 800 women. Someone clasps her hand and guides her to a seat at the front of the room, those reserved for the *deputation. On the stage, Mrs Pethick-Lawrence waits for silence. 'They thought the women of this country were inured to political subjection; they have found out their mistake. The worm has turned at last.' Marie is riveted as Mrs Pethick-Lawrence and Christabel speak for almost two hours, inspiring everyone with their revolutionary fervour.*

GLASS - SMASHING FOR VOTES! SUFFRAGETTES AS WINDOW - BREAKERS.

At 6.15pm Marie shuffles towards the door, staying close to her small group of three. Some head north to Oxford Street but her companion grasps her arm and guides her along the Strand, past Charing Cross station to

Trafalgar Square. More women peel off, heading for Regent Street but Marie turns left into Whitehall, to position herself outside her target, the Home Office. She waits for her cue.

The cry goes up. 'Votes for Women'. From in front, behind, from every side comes a hammering, crashing, splintering sound. A hasty glance sees a policeman hurrying towards her. She feels in her pocket, grasps the stone, and throws.

Her arm is grabbed. The policeman's grip tightens as he propels her through the London streets towards Bow Street Court where women are spilling out of the building. They cheer as she joins the throng. Then the call comes. Ushers push and pull them until every nook and cranny of the courtroom is filled. The Magistrate, Mr Curtis Bennett, scans the room, nods to the clerk, and prepares himself to weather the inevitable cries of 'Votes for Women' as he processes the prisoners.

Marie waits her turn. She finds herself alongside Olive Wharry, from Holsworthy, a familiar face from the Church League for Women's Suffrage.

'First time?' Olive asks.

'Yes.'

'Who are you?'

'You know who I am, Marie Newby from Ilfracombe.'

'I know, but he don't.' She nods at the magistrate. 'You've family at home. Might want to think of an alias.'

'Alias?'

'Joyce Locke, pleased to meet you,' Olive holds out her hand in mock greeting. Olive, Joyce, winks as an usher grabs her arm and pushes her towards the rail. Women cheer as she raises her hand in salute.

Marie shuffles forward in line, her alias ready. There will be no record in the papers of the arrest of Mrs Kathleen Marie Anstice du Sautoy Newby. She is less prepared for the sentence. Two months imprisonment with hard labour. She gasps. Two months is bad enough but the hard labour means she will be denied her own clothes, time to exercise and speak with others.

She is about to experience Holloway at its worst. Lined up against the stone wall, she watches as warders make their way along the line towards her. No amount of fine words or mental preparation is enough to withstand the violation of harsh hands reaching inside her dress, tugging at her underwear, leaving her publicly naked, humiliated, shamed. And this is only the beginning.

Marie is thrust into a dark cell, much like that described by Daisy Solomon in Prisons and Prisoners, the autobiography of aristocratic suffragette, Constance Lytton:

> In the cell - a shelf near the door which is honoured by the name of table, a wooden chair, and standing up against the wall, a plank bed. Then at the far end of the cell there is a hot water pipe, and on the floor a row of tins, a dustpan and brush, small basin, tin to hold water, a pail, also - a plate. On a low shelf there is a bundle of bedding consisting of a thin, hard mattress and an even harder pillow, two blankets, a pair of sheets, and a sort of rug. The shelf above contains a slate and pencil, a case with the prison rules, a mug, spoon, salt-cellar, and toothbrush. There, too, one finds a Bible, hymn book, prayer book, "The Narrow Way", "A Healthy Home and How to Keep It", and a brush and comb.

Confined in separate cells, the suffragettes smash windows to call to each other, anything to bolster their resolve as they prepare to go on hunger strike. Hunger strike, a phrase familiar to Marie from reading *Votes for Women* sitting in a comfortable armchair by her fireside. But here, within the stark, cold walls of Holloway, the reality is very different. The hunger pangs are the first to assault her, intensified by the sweet-smelling food left in her cell to tempt her to eat. When this fails, the harrowing noises from adjacent cells bring her to breaking point.

Soon after starting her hunger strike, Margaret Macfarlane is singled out for the horror of force-feeding. She recalls:

> I was lifted into a chair and tied with a strong sheet to the back of the chair. As far as I can remember, my arms were held on each side on the arms of the chair. There was a wardress with a feeding cup and one behind my chair, making a gag for the mouth with her fingers. Another held my knees. I told them that I would not swallow a drop of the gruel voluntarily. When they found that I did not retain any of the food, the one who was gagging me egged

the others on to tickle me, to hold my nose to make me swallow, and to grip me on the throat, which to me is the most cruel. The pressing of the throat to make one swallow gives a fearful feeling of suffocation. When they got my feet up, my head was hanging right over the back of the chair, which added to the choking sensation.

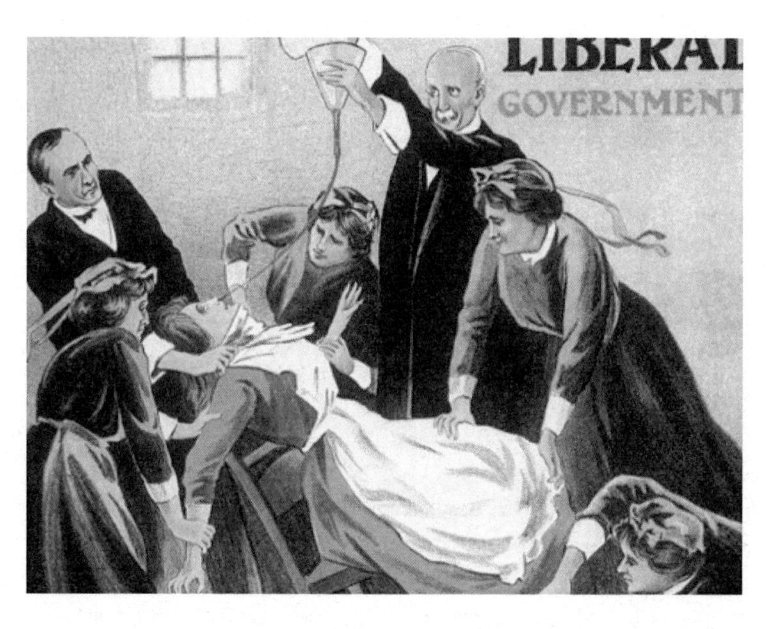

Ada Cecile Wright, also arrested at the same time as Marie, gives an even more graphic description:

When the hour of torture arrived, the door of my cell was suddenly flung open, and four to six or seven officers entered and seized me. There was a deep breathless struggle while I clung to my iron bedstead, and held on to it with all my strength. I was against five or six, but it was always some minutes before the wardresses, after using much force and pressure, could unlock me from that position. Naturally I got much bruised, but of that I do not complain, as bruises were mutual. I was then dragged to the chair, and tied down and my hands and arms were tightly held by wardresses on each side so that I could not move.

Two doctors now came in and began their objectionable work. One stood behind me and one in front, and they proceeded to force open my jaw. When my lips had first been forced open, a steel gage was, with force again, on the one side and resistance on the other, inserted between my teeth and my mouth was then prised open, and kept so by the doctor behind, who worked the gag and who held my head so that I could not move it, while the doctor in front rammed that unspeakable instrument of disgust and torture - so to me, at least - the stomach tube, down my throat, causing me to writhe and retch and cough and choke at every twist with which he sent it down. At first it absolutely used to suffocate me till I grew almost black in the face for want of breath.

Once during the first hunger strike, I am fully convinced it did actually get into my windpipe; my feet and my hands were firmly held, and I was pinioned to the ground, but so awful was the sense of suffocation that in one desperate attempt I writhed myself free and the tube was withdrawn. After the doctor had sent down the tube the steel gag was withdrawn from the side of my jaw, and a wooden gag was slipped between my teeth instead. This gag was discarded later, as the doctor found I could use my tongue to press against the tube and close the passage. He then used to put his finger in my mouth and hold my tongue.

A wardress now poured the food down the tube when all the time I would be choking and retching ...

As the hour of the forced feeding drew near, I could not help being deeply agitated, in spite of myself, and I used to stand or sit or walk about in a state of horrible suspense, with my heart thumping against my ribs, and listen to the footsteps of the doctors and wardresses as they walked to and fro and passed from cell to cell, and to the cries and groans of those who were being fed until at last the steps paused at my door, and it was thrown open, faces appeared in the doorway and my turn had come!

While inside, the women, including Marie somehow managed to pass a handkerchief between them recording their imprisonment. Her signature is bottom left, upside down.

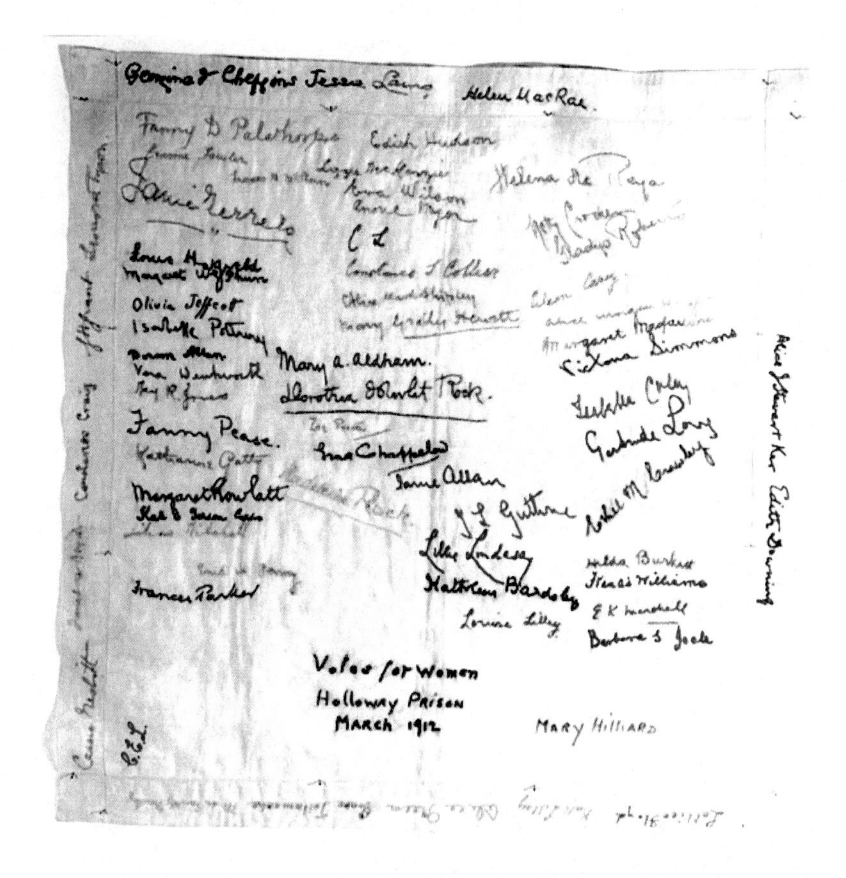

The women who signed alongside her included:

Vera Wentworth: who was forcibly fed by nasal tube before being released at the end of June.

Katherine Gatty: sentenced to six months for breaking £42 worth of glass, four months more than an Edinburgh man who broke his wife's skull.

Alice Green: who, when sentenced said: 'Let me tell you what I have gone through lately on behalf of this cause. I have given up my home, my husband and my child and I shall not go back until women get the vote.' She was forcibly fed through a nasal tube.

Alice Maud Shipley: who also spoke out at her trial: 'More than half my life I have been doing what lies in me to help the poor and unfortunate. I feel our case is a most urgent one, and I feel that only a woman can understand a woman's needs, that women suffer for the want and care of men, and that their salvation lies in looking after their own needs and in demanding the vote'. Sentenced to four months. She went on hunger strike and was forcibly fed.

Alice Parker: niece of Lord Kitchener and WSPU organiser for Glasgow said at her trial, 'If I had thrown a stone as a striker, or even as a man who is intoxicated, I suppose I should have received a very light sentence; for I have noticed that men in Swansea, when they were held up for rioting, got a fortnight's imprisonment, and the ringleader of them got only six weeks.' Sentenced to four months.

Victoria Simmons: left school in Bristol at fourteen because her father believed daughters should not receive the same education as sons and spent many years campaigning for equality in education. Sentenced to two months for breaking a window at the War Office.

Grace Tollamache: joint Hon. Secretary of the Bath branch of the WSPU. Sentenced to two months.

Zoe Proctor: Like many of the women, she came from an affluent background and initially had trouble adapting to prison routine. Much to the amusement of the other prisoners she expected her bed to be made for her. Sentenced to two months.

Others also sentenced to Holloway were:

Vera Wentworth: who at her trial said she would do the same thing again and possibly worse. Sentenced to six months.

Emily Davison: one of the most committed of all suffragettes and someone who often acted alone and without the approval of the WSPU leadership. She was a committed hunger striker and barricaded herself in her cell to resist force-feeding. The prison governor had to authorise the use of a water cannon to end the protest. However, she was seriously injured when she threw herself down a prison staircase and was in hospital when the handkerchief was signed.

Kitty Marion: At her trial she demanded the vote so that the country could be made civilised and Christian, and for the protection of women and children. Sentenced to six months for breaking windows at a jewellers and Messr Sainsbury and Co. in Regent Street. If this was meant as a deterrent they underestimated Kitty Marion. Just a few months after her release she was back with a vengeance - in North Devon.

We don't know if Marie endured force-feeding but she did go on hunger strike. As she finally emerged through the gates of Holloway at the end of her sentence, she was presented with a WSPU medal 'For Valour'. Her name was inscribed on the reverse, and presented in a silk-lined case with a gold blocked inscription on the lid: 'Presented to Marie du Sautoy Newby by the Women's Social & Political Union in recognition of a gallant action, whereby through endurance to the last extremity of hunger and hardship a great principle of political justice was vindicated.'

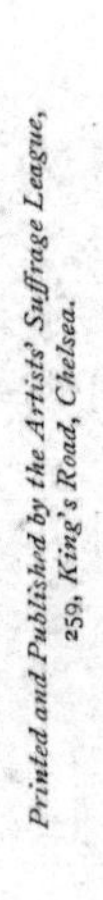

Chapter Fourteen

Barnstaple's Man of Principle

Summer into Autumn 1912

The violent protests in March provoked a backlash. Trying times began for the WSPU when police raided their headquarters with warrants for the arrest of Mr and Mrs Pethick-Lawrence, Mrs Pankhurst and Christabel. Christabel evaded arrest by fleeing the country. She exiled herself to France, recalling Annie to take charge in London. But it was delegation in name only. Christabel clung on to control, insisting Annie travel to Paris for weekly briefings. Her obsession with holding onto power was fuelled by paranoia that others were plotting to challenge her leadership. It seemed she had lost her political flair, dismissing organisers like Mary Phillips - one of her most dedicated supporters. Several women went to Paris to remonstrate with her but found her changed, wearing smart Parisian clothes and treating their visits dismissively.

There were other, more immediate effects. Although the WSPU had dismissed the original Conciliation Bill as being dead in the water, it still came before Parliament on March 28th. At the vote, the previous substantial majorities evaporated and the Bill failed to pass its second reading. The Women's Freedom League [WFL] were in no doubt why: 'There is little doubt the Bill would have passed its second reading if it had not been for the recent militancy. Many MPs who voted against the second reading or abstained declared that their action was a protest against militant methods and not a final judgement on the general question.

'It is impossible to view this defeat with any other feeling than the deepest pain and regret. The woman's movement in Britain has received an undoubted blow. We cannot and do not share the view that it is a good thing the Bill is killed. The WSPU have said repeatedly that they were not interested in the Bill and did not care whether it was defeated or not. Indeed, it seems likely that the militancy which took place only three weeks before this critical second reading was deliberately designed to wreck the Bill.' The cracks in the militant movement were deepening, and the WFL was in no doubt that the blame lay in the increasing recklessness of the WSPU.

The Ilfracombe entry in *Votes for Women* carried a brief reference to Marie's part in the recent militancy. 'The Hon Treasurer is unable to carry out her usual work as she is serving a sentence of two months hard labour for breaking a Government window, value only £2.' But Marie's absence didn't mean activity came to a halt. It was the end of the financial year and Anne Ball again refused to pay her taxes. The Tax Resistance League reported her stand: 'A Tax-Resistance Sale of goods seized from Miss Ball, Matron of the Trained Nurses Institute of Ilfracombe and Barnstaple, took place recently at the Auction Rooms, High-street, Barnstaple. A previous sale had taken place a fortnight earlier at Ilfracombe. Members of different suffrage societies were present, and leaflets were distributed. The tax collectors and other officials concerned in the distraint and sales have invariably acted with the greatest kindness and courtesy, and seem fully to grasp the principle of tax resistance as practised by the women of the Tax Resistance League.'

Anne also stepped up to host the group's regular meetings: 'A most successful 'At Home' was held last Saturday through the kindness of Miss Ball who acted as Hostess. Mrs Curtis made an impressive speech on the horrors of the White Slave Traffic. Many thanks to Miss Ross for her splendid help.'

By June 7th, 1912, Marie was back and making arrangements for their next public meeting. Significantly the speaker was Georgina Brackenbury who was sentenced alongside Marie for the March window-smashing campaign. It was a nostalgic return to the West Country for Georgina. In 1909 she had been part of Annie Kenney's team working alongside Vera Wentworth and Mary Blathwayt.

Surprisingly perhaps, Marie's prison experience isn't referred to again in *Votes for Women;* it was simply business as usual with a welcome to the new faces in the group and delight that sales of the paper were up thanks to the efforts of Miss Ross. Prison hadn't undermined Marie's dedication to the WSPU. The next week she was advertising for 'any visitors to the town willing to help by distributing handbills or paper selling at the meeting on Thursday 20. Those wishing for invitation cards for the 'At Home' should apply at once.'

The meeting was postponed by a week but on the afternoon of Thursday, June 27th the Gaiety Hall at Ilfracombe was filled with women eager to hear Georgina Brackenbury. And if they missed out on an invitation to that event, they had a second chance. At 8pm she was again in action addressing a crowd at Montebello Lawn, the venue at the back of the Gaiety where visitors traditionally gathered for Ilfracombe's season of summer concerts.

Things were going well. Membership was growing, prestigious speakers were regularly finding their way to this Devon backwater, and they had a candidate for the Barnstaple constituency, Henry D. Harben, who was brave enough to stand and be counted when it came to Votes for Women. But his support of the cause was about to deprive them of a valuable ally.

In June 1912, the Labour politician George Lansbury confronted Asquith in the House of Commons denouncing the government for their treatment of Suffragist prisoners: 'You are beneath contempt. You call yourselves gentlemen, yet forcibly feed and murder women in this fashion. You ought to be driven out of public life. It is the most disgraceful thing that has happened in the history of England. You will go down in posterity as a man who condemned innocent women. You will be remembered as a Government that has tortured women.'

It was a stand that resonated with Henry Harben, prompting him to write to the Barnstaple Liberal Association withdrawing his candidature in protest against the forcible feeding of suffragist prisoners and the Government's proposal to give more votes to men, while leaving women unenfranchised. He wrote: 'what is the good of it all? If the authorities want to vindicate the law, let them first avoid making it ridiculous. If they only want to treble the income of the WSPU they might find some more humane way of doing it. This policy of pusillanimous persecution is not my idea of Liberalism. The bullying of voteless women by a Government that is actually proposing to widen the franchise of men is quite without excuse. Unmanly, ungentlemanly, unsportsmanlike, and uncivilised it can serve no purpose but to disgrace those who are responsible for it and those who acquiesce in it. The Liberal party in the House of Commons having endorsed this policy, I feel compelled to make the only protest open to me by withdrawing my active support altogether from the party at the present time.'

The leadership of the WSPU were jubilant, applauding his actions in surrendering the chance of a safe Liberal seat. The Ilfracombe group was quick to add its support: 'A great impression has been made here by the splendid action of Mr Harben in resigning his Parliamentary candidature as a protest. It has brought home to a good many people the abominable treatment of suffragist prisoners by the so called Liberal Government.'

Just three months later they had cause to regret their enthusiasm.

Meanwhile, the summer passed with the usual round of garden meetings and 'At Homes', now increasingly hosted by Anne Ball with the help of Miss Ross. Their key attraction during the holiday campaign of 1912 was Dr Christine Murrell, a significant figure in the medical world. She was only the second woman to be appointed House Physician at the Royal Free Hospital and, unusually for a woman at the time, ran her own general practice in Bayswater. In-between seeing patients, attending Infant Welfare Clinics and lecturing for the London County Council and other bodies, she was an enthusiastic advocate for the WSPU. When considering invitations to speak, it may have been Ilfracombe's pedigree as a summer constitutional hotspot that won her over.

The group found a novel way of attracting attention on Regatta day when they decorated a pony carriage and drove it around the town and pier. And they didn't miss a trick when it came to selling copies of *Votes for Women*. One volunteer brought along her very endearing eight-year-old daughter.

Other pro-suffrage speakers were also in North Devon. Just down the road in Braunton a Mr Mitchell and Miss Tyte addressed a large crowd at the Cross Tree, a 300 year old Elm in the centre of the village, the traditional site for open air gatherings and activities.

But it wasn't long before Mr Harben's resignation was the topic of conversation again, and being viewed with nostalgia. In October

Mr H. A. Baker was adopted as the new Liberal candidate. Tragically, his views on women's suffrage could not have been more different. He stated he: 'could not pledge himself to vote for women's suffrage if returned. It was not in the interests of women or the country. There was no evidence the majority of women wanted such a change.' The women of the Barnstaple constituency were now saddled with a confirmed anti-suffragist.

Undaunted, those gathered for the AGM of the Devon Women's Liberal Association, held in Bideford, begged: 'all members of Parliament who desire the well-being of the country to support such amendments to the Reform Bill as shall place the self-protecting power of the vote in the hands of women.' But this was tempered by the now familiar reservation. 'Rational, logical plans for female enfranchisement have been hampered by misguided women going about the country in the name of militant suffragists. Despite them, the great principle will be carried into law. We mean to struggle for the vote until we have it.'

Sadly their concerted voice made no difference to Mr Baker who couldn't have been more dismissive. He announced that he didn't intend to deal with several questions handed to him on Women's Suffrage, remarking that it was evident the views of the questioners differed from his own. It was staggering paternalism and insufferable arrogance all rolled into one but there is no doubt that militancy was creating a backlash. Marguerite Norma-Smith, now working for the NUWSS in Yorkshire, commented: 'The last militant outbreak is making work here terribly difficult. It really is sad!'

Undaunted, the Barnstaple NUWSS forged ahead with a garden meeting in the Castle grounds. Kate James was still very much involved, seconding a motion calling on the Government to pass an enfranchisement measure during the present session. They were also looking further ahead, to a suffrage summer school being held on Dartmoor in August or September. Names for this were invited by the group's new organiser, Miss Christine Wodehouse, someone already well known for her work with young people in her father's parish at Bratton Fleming - and even more famous for her family connections. She was a cousin of author and humorist, P.G. Wodehouse.

Meanwhile, the 'misguided women' of the WSPU were on the move to bigger, better, more imposing premises at Lincoln's Inn House, Kingsway. According to *Votes for Women,* this five storey, Portland Stone edifice built in Italian Renaissance style 'stands out even among the other fine buildings in the street', an interesting reflection on the importance of appearances. A lack of space at Clements Inn, also the home of the Pethick-Lawrence's, was given as the reason for the move. But a statement issued just two weeks later offered a very different view.

Along with Mrs Pankhurst, Mr and Mrs Pethick-Lawrence had been sentenced to nine months after the window-smashing campaign. They joined all those arrested on hunger strike, and suffered the violence of force feeding. Mrs Pethick-Lawrence resisted so vigorously it took nine wardresses to hold her down. Frederick Pethick-Lawrence suffered force-feeding twice a day for ten days before being released in a state of near collapse. They travelled to Canada soon afterwards to recuperate and reflect. They were becoming increasingly concerned about the direction the WSPU was taking. They opposed the mass window-smashing and feared this was only the tip of the iceberg. It was time to speak out. When they returned in early October it was to a mixed homecoming.

Christabel and Emmeline made it clear that they intended to pursue a new militant policy of all-out war against the government, inciting WSPU members to strike however they could, particularly through the destruction of property. On this they were intransigent. *Votes for Women* reported: 'At the first reunion of the leaders after the enforced holiday, Mrs Pankhurst and Miss Christabel Pankhurst outlined a new militant policy, which Mr and Mrs Pethick-Lawrence found themselves altogether unable to approve. Mrs Pankhurst and Miss Christabel Pankhurst indicated that they were not prepared to modify their intentions and recommended that Mr and Mrs Pethick-

Lawrence should resume control of the paper *Votes for Women* and leave the Women's Social and Political Union.'

Christabel and Emmeline had combined to oust two core supporters of the movement who had been alongside them every step of the way. Rather than create a schism in the ranks, Mr and Mrs Pethick-Lawrence agreed to go quietly. It was the first of several expulsions that eventually even included Sylvia and Adela. Their warnings that Christabel's tactics were undermining support for the movement were seen as signs that they were about to set up a counter organisation. The Pankhurst family splintered, seen by Mrs Pankhurst and Christabel as unavoidable collateral damage.

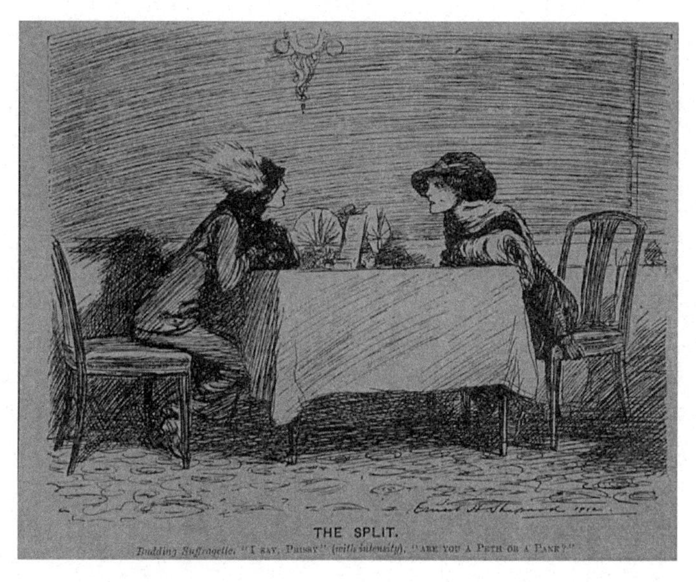

THE SPLIT
Budding Suffragette. "I say Patsy" (*with intensity*) "Are you a Peth or a Pank?"

Others saw the expulsions very differently, Evelina Haverfield among them. She transferred her loyalties to Sylvia and her work in the East End of London. But surprisingly, despite all the disquiet, there were no mass resignations from the WSPU. Active workers remained loyal, including Marie Newby and the members of the

Ilfracombe and Barnstaple group. The only observable difference was that their regular reports now appeared in the WSPU's new publication, *The Suffragette*.

Ilfracombe's first entry under the new regime was notice of a charabanc to be run to Barnstaple for a public meeting at the Albert Hall on the topic of White Slave Traffic. It was quite a coup with not only one but three speakers; Miss Abadam, Rev Hatty Baker and the Rev G.H. Davis. Alice Abadam was a unique figure in the Women's Suffrage movement in that she moved easily between the increasing number of suffrage organisations. She spoke with wit, intelligence and passion on women's struggle for a political voice: 'Whereas by charitable tinkering they may remedy individual lives, by laying their hands on the political machine they would influence the lives of millions of their poorer and unprotected sisters for good.' She was a prolific writer on women's oppression, dealing with issues ranging from women's employment to the subject of this debate, the white slave trade.

Alice Abadam was supported by the Reverend Hatty Baker, co-founder of the Free Church League for Women's Suffrage. She was a controversial figure within the church, convinced that women should trust in their own vision of God, not rely on a version handed down by men. For her, this spiritual independence reached much further than the institution of the church. She saw it as an essential step towards equality in all aspects of women's lives, including their fight for the vote. Together they made a formidable team.

Articles in the new magazine, *The Suffragette,* became ever more militant following the split within the innermost ranks of the WSPU. They also had a new aim - to make life, not only for the government but all electors, so unbearable that they would give women the vote to put an end to the disruption.

Sylvia Pankhurst gave a breathtaking summary of this escalation of violence from petty injuries and annoyances to large-scale damage:

Street lamps were broken, 'Votes for Women' was painted on the seats at Hampstead Heath, keyholes were stopped up with lead pellets, house numbers were painted out, chairs flung in the Serpentine, cushions of railway carriages slashed, flower-beds damaged, golf greens all over the country scraped and burnt with acid. A bowling green was cut in Glasgow, the turf in Duthie Park, Aberdeen.

A mother and daughter, bearing an ancient name, spent much of their time travelling in trains in order to drop pebbles between the sashes of carriage windows, hoping the glass would smash on being raised. Old ladies applied for gun licences to terrify the authorities. Bogus telephone messages were sent calling up the Army Reserves and Territorials. Telegraph and telephone wires were severed with long-handled clippers; fuse boxes were blown up, communication between London and Glasgow being cut for some hours.

There was a window-smashing raid in West End club-land; the Carlton, the Junior Carlton, the Reform Club and others being attacked. A large envelope containing red pepper and snuff was sent to every Cabinet Minister; the Press reported that they all fell victims to the ruse.

The WSPU also escalated a campaign to destroy the contents of pillar-boxes. May Billinghurst was the driving force, setting out in a wheelchair with a rug concealing packages oozing a dark brown sticky fluid. She went from one pillar box to the next dropping a package into each one. The government claimed over 5,000 letters were damaged this way.

And this was only the beginning.

Chapter Fifteen
Rebuffed
January 1913

The New Year saw a flurry of activity in North Devon. Women's Liberal Associations across the area had historically backed their candidates, with the ladies throwing themselves into campaigning whenever the call came. But their new candidate's stance on women's suffrage, and his emphatic rebuff at their AGM, pushed them into unprecedented action. Most of these women were not suffragettes, or even suffragists, but they issued a public challenge:

Dear Sir,

We the undersigned Liberal women, note with great regret your views against the enfranchisement of women.

We think you lost sight of the fact - amongst others - that in the event of your being returned to Parliament as member for this Division, a considerable part of your salary would be forcibly obtained from women who feel strongly the injustice of taxation without representation.

We are, of course, aware our present member has consistently voted in favour of Women Suffrage, and urged the justice of their claim. We could, therefore only regard the election of an anti-suffragist as a distinctly retrograde step which would make it very difficult, in some cases impossible, for us to work in the Liberal interest in future.

We beg you will give the subject your further serious consideration and hope you may find it possible to modify your views on the subject.

Mr Baker did not mince his words. He replied that he did not approve of the Parliamentary vote being extended to women, and would not in any way bind himself to help them to get it. The women of Ilfracombe probably regretted applauding Henry Harben's principled resignation now. What a different reception he would have given them.

The ladies' letter was published in the Ilfracombe Gazette, prompting a response from someone who signed himself 'Junius'. He had very definite views on the women's uncertainty about working for Liberal interests in the future: 'May I be allowed to argue that such a consequence is a very unwise result? ... To refuse to support Liberalism ... seems to me to be the height of unwisdom ... what guarantee is there that the Tories would accede to the demands of the women? The social reforms that are still necessary will never come from the Tories ... therefore any woman (or man) who ... withholds help from the only party of progress - the Liberals -

thereby does just so much to assist a retrograde party without any policy or convictions, save a desire itself to climb into office.'

In what feels like deliberate provocation or staggering paternalism, Junius goes on to refer to the women as 'people with fads and crotchets,' and 'legislative hobbies.' It was a step too far. The following week a letter appeared from an 'Ex-Liberal':

> Dear Sir,
> ... We absolutely refuse to have such a fundamental and world-wide question as the enfranchisement of women relegated contemptuously to the ranks of "legislative hobbies, fads and crotchets". If poor Junius has made this classification honestly and in good faith, I can only assure him that he is in the most pitiable state of ignorance as to the extent and strength of the movement for the enfranchisement of women. Women are not clamouring for the recognition of fads and crotchets; they are demanding, as men once did, justice, liberty and equality. A Liberal Government has consistently thwarted them in this demand, with the inevitable outcome that women in constantly increasing numbers are separating themselves from this party, as I myself did some time ago.
>
> ... Why should they (Liberal Women) help to keep in power a Government that regards them all as political non-entities? ... Their work has been gratefully accepted, nay, begged for, but when a fair return for their work is mentioned, they are told to run away and play a little longer, until the men have finished their own more important concerns ... As I am politically non-existent (except when the tax collector calls or insurance money is due) I naturally expect this letter will be non existent in the next edition of the *Ilfracombe Chronicle*.

Her letter did appear, but anonymously. Given the emphatic tone, Anne or Marie are strong possibilities. Another member of the group, Margaret Eldridge, had no compunction about signing her name to a second letter: 'We hope by refusing to do anything for

Anti-Suffrage candidates we may stir the sluggish conscience of the whole party on this subject, and awaken them to our great need ... Do men fear women will corrupt politics? ... It is not a question of rivalry as many seem to think. Co-operation will prove to be a mutual aid, men will be benefited by the new order of things quite as much as women, and perhaps a century hence they will admit it.'

Week three and Junius is back, making a stab at contrition. 'If I used any words which my critics think may belittle their views, I wish to express my regret, as no one doubts their sincerity, even if not agreeing with them.' He then quotes Sir Edward Grey to justify his view. 'You cannot form a Cabinet from either of the existing parties which would be completely in favour of Women's Suffrage, and have a united party behind it. The disappearance of this Government would only mean a government coming in from the other side which would be as much divided. The question would not be advanced.'

Immediately beneath this response from Junius is another, much longer, letter signed by Richard Havilland of Chambercombe, Ilfracombe, the first pro-suffrage man, though anti-militancy, to enter the debate in the press since Mr Mortlock-Brown of Braunton:

> Dear Sir,
> John Stuart Mill held to it, in all seriousness, and as a part of practical politics, that: "Women ought to be treated as beings equal in intelligence to, and having rights equally with man, and should no longer be classed with children and idiots and lunatics, who need to have everything done for them." That being so in the time of Mill, when the masses were so illiterate, how much more true is it at the present time, when education has made such strides.

Mr Havilland goes on to point out some facts to their Conservative candidate:

> ... the opponents of female suffrage so often fall back on the vague and unsatisfactory reason that they refuse the vote

> because "men are men and women (intellectually) women" … but woman is intellectual enough to be taxed: she has been found intellectual enough to sit on the British throne more than once … to be schoolmistress, doctor of medicine, civil servant and voter at municipal, school board, county council and other elections. Yet it is asserted that she is incapable of equal intelligence with the town and country elector whose "intellectuality" consists, it is very often alleged, in discovering the candidate who will give him the biggest jug of ale. Or again with the many electors who are even now classed as illiterates, being unable to read the English language on the ballot papers!

Cries of 'hear, hear!' are sure to have rung round Anne Ball's sitting room. Mr Havilland's arguments are not new, but for them to be voiced so publicly by a man was welcome support for the Ilfracombe suffragettes. Many sentences will have been savoured at their next meeting. He continues: '… generations of men have confessed that they could not understand women. And yet they have gone on legislating for her … Men and women are alike citizens of the state, alike contribute to its strength and security, and alike are entitled to a voice in its destinies and their own.'

But then the subject of militancy rears its head: 'If the militants have been to a certain extent too demonstrative they have suffered very severely for their cause, not the least of which has been to brave public ridicule. But we must not lose sight of the fact that the non-militant has been quietly and laboriously pursuing her way, leaving no time for breaking the windows of disobliging Cabinet Ministers and other stirring enterprises.'

Mr Havilland gets into his stride on militancy in another letter the following week: 'It is to be hoped that Members of Parliament will decide their action on the broad merits of the question, and not allow themselves to be influenced by the outcry - perhaps not so unreasonable in itself - against the criminal excesses of Militancy gone mad … But for the suicidal policy of the Militant party during the last few years in deliberately flouting and estranging the more moderate party, on whose votes they are bound mainly to rely, the question of female franchise would have stood today on a much firmer basis.'

Militancy gone mad. Suicidal policy. Harsh words not helped by references to 'inflammatory effusions, which of course appeal to the more ambitious and excitable among the Suffragettes.' But he continues: 'However do not let us be influenced by considerations which have nothing to do with the subject. So let bygones be bygones.'

His views stir Marie to write again, this time publicly identifying herself as a militant. It is our first opportunity to hear her speaking in her own words:

> Dear Sir - One hears much of the Militant Suffragists and what they are doing, may I say a few words on the need for such militancy. First of all I should like to mention why we militants are so keen on getting the vote that we are ready to leave our homes - and most suffragettes have very happy home relations - for prisons. We know that the women, with the power of the vote behind them, working with the men, would be able to improve existing conditions. For surely questions concerning housing, children's welfare etc would be better understood by the former. Take Bow and Bromley alone and the awful lives of the poor there. Think of the thousands and thousands of sweated women workers, the overcrowded slum dwellings, the children who grow up stunted in mind and body and, last but not least, think that the average age of girls entrapped in the White Slave Traffic throughout the world is only eight years old. Authorities tell us that in spite of the Criminal Law Amendment Act - which Act, as the *Daily News and Leader* said, was only passed through as a sop to the suffragists - much more will have to be done to stop this vile trade.
>
> Then there is the injustice of the laws. For example, take those relating to injury to person - a few weeks imprisonment for the men who assault little girls if they have not already been let

off with a fine, and those relating to damage to property - months of imprisonment for breaking a window! I should like to ask those gentlemen who say: "I have always been in favour of Woman Suffrage, but will do nothing *now* to help because of this militancy", a question. What did they do to help the women before they were militant? The answer, in most cases, is *nothing*. During the forty-five years of constitutional agitation, they either had not heard of the demand for Woman Suffrage or else they did not take it seriously. If they had done their best there would have been no necessity for militancy.

A gentleman of Cambridge said to one of our speakers the other day, "Convert the electors." She answered, "You are an elector and you say you are converted, but what have you done for us, have you even let your representative in Parliament know that you are in favour of women being enfranchised? To which he had to reply in the negative. Many say war is a necessary evil, and yet in every war damage is done to private property and thousands of "innocent" people are rendered homeless. Remember no windows were broken or other damage done until time after time women were arrested and imprisoned as common felons for going quietly on deputations to the House of Commons, which any man is permitted to do, and not only arrested but knocked about and disgracefully treated, not by the crowd who are favourable, with the exception of a few hooligans, but by the police who had their orders. I am not blaming the police as a Force, they are splendid men, and great friends of the suffragettes, but amongst any large body of people some will be always found who would behave as brutes if occasion permitted, and some times as many as 20,000 police have been called out to "protect" the Houses of Parliament.

We do not wish those concerned to like it if their windows are broken or their game of golf spoilt. Have our non-militant friends ever heard of the London bus-driver, until then perfectly indifferent to the political enfranchisement of women, who, being held up by a suffrage procession shouted in tones of

> exasperation, "Oh! Give 'em the vote, but don't let them stop the traffic."
>
> Yours faithfully, M.du Sautoy Newby. Hon Sec. WSPU

There is no doubt where Marie stood on the issue. But any hope she had of galvanising public opinion was undermined as soon as readers turned to the next page and read the headline: '*Suffragettes Mean Trick - Ilfracombe Victims*. One of the latest dodges worked by the spiteful members of the "Votes for Women" party, was carried out this week all over the country, by means of letters posted in several of the large towns of the North of England. The method adopted was to wrap a halfpenny in a leaflet advocating Woman Suffrage, and post the letter without a stamp ... On Wednesday, a number of such trick letters were delivered at Ilfracombe, each involving a payment of 6d.'

The letter contained a leaflet asking anyone annoyed, inconvenienced or financially injured by the tactics of the suffragettes to remind themselves of women's fight for the vote. A familiar message, but with a fundamental change in tone and target:

> The Government that withholds this reform is our arch-enemy. By every means in our power we are making it impossible for them to continue to govern women without their consent. Many think that our actions hit chiefly at people who are innocent in the matter. There are few who have had no opportunity of informing themselves as to the justice of our cause, and the glaring reason for urgency, If the public will not rise and demand for women their emancipation, they cannot complain if they receive some of the knocks when the women are fighting their own battle. All these tactics that you perhaps so much dislike will instantly cease directly you demand Votes for Women and get it. Your would-be fellow citizen, A Suffragette.

The Chronicle was defiant 'These spiteful tricks will most certainly not make the public "rise and demand for women their emancipation" but will retard the movement. Voters will not be bullied into any course of conduct by methods of terrorism …' Many Ilfracombe readers will have agreed. What did the suffragettes hope to gain by antagonising ordinary people? Did they think the citizens of Britain would rise as one to demand that the Government end this nuisance and give women the vote? Whatever the reasoning, many began to question the escalation of tactics, particularly into militancy, that had already caused the organisation to fracture at its very heart.

For over a year Asquith had sounded like a broken record promising that the Reform Bill would be open to free amendment to include women suffrage. The more optimistic campaigners of the NUWSS had silenced their reservations and taken him at his word. They were about to receive an emphatic wake-up call.

Asquith had made a rod for his own back by procrastinating with his promise of a free amendment. He couldn't deny time for his own Bill. So he looked for another way to sabotage his personal promise. Asquith approached the Speaker of the House of Commons, James William Lowther, for a ruling on the effect of the amendments before they were discussed in order to avoid 'the sense of unreality' and 'the abortive employment of parliamentary time.' Surprise, surprise, the Speaker concluded that if the women's amendments were passed it would add a very large class to the electorate and establish an entirely new principle. Therefore, he was driven to the conclusion that it would practically constitute a new Bill. With staggering pretence, Asquith thanked the Speaker for saving the House from what would have been a regrettable waste of Parliamentary time.

It was the end of the Bill and marked the beginning of a more destructive, more indiscriminate campaign than ever before. And top of the list was a new tactic that would inflame divisions. Arson.

MORE ARSON BY WILD WOMEN.

Bristol University's athletic pavilion, which has been destroyed by fire. It is supposed to be the work of suffragettes. The building was only erected two years ago at a cost of £2,000.

Chapter Sixteen
Wild Women
February into March 1913

'It was at this time, February 1913, less than two years ago as I write these words,' wrote Sylvia Pankhurst, 'that militancy, as it is now generally understood by the public, began - militancy in the sense of continued, destructive, guerrilla warfare against the Government through injury to private property. Some property had been destroyed before this time, but the attacks were sporadic, and were meant to be in the nature of a warning as to what might become a settled policy. Now we indeed lighted the torch, and we did it with the absolute conviction that no other course was open to us ... we had to do as much of this guerilla warfare as the people of England would tolerate.' These words heralded a time of unprecedented destruction.

The women of the WSPU had crossed a line, graphically described by Sylvia Pankhurst:

> When the campaign was fully underway, certain officials of the Union were given, as their main work, the task of advising incendiaries, and arranging for the supply of such inflammable material, house-breaking tools and other matter as they might require. A certain, exceedingly feminine looking young lady (Grace Roe) was strolling about London, meeting militants in all sorts of public and unexpected places, to arrange for perilous expeditions. Women, most of them very young, toiled through the night across unfamiliar country, carrying heavy cases of petrol and paraffin. Sometimes they failed, sometimes succeeded in setting fire to an untenanted building - all the better if it were the residence of a notability - or a church, or other place of historic interest.

Attempts were made to burn the houses of two MPs who opposed women having the vote. These failed but then, on 19 February 1913 two suffragettes made their final preparations to attack their most strategic target yet. A second home was being built for Lloyd George next to the Walton Heath golf course in Surrey. Just two weeks earlier, Lloyd George had refused to see a deputation of suffragettes to discuss the vote, making himself a prime target for reprisals. In the early hours, they broke into the house and left two bombs on timers. One detonated causing extensive damage but another failed to ignite. The WSPU always insisted that their actions would never harm anyone. Lloyd George's house was empty; but workmen had been due to arrive around 6am. The crude detonation techniques could easily have resulted in the bombs exploding when they were on the site, with deadly consequences.

Speaking in Cardiff the following day, Mrs Pankhurst declared: 'we have blown up the Chancellor of the Exchequer's house, a way of trying to wake up his conscience'. She was unrepentant, firmly convinced that the only way to get the vote was to make things intolerable for most people in the country so that they would demand MPs get rid of the nuisance. Significantly she declared: 'for all that has been done in the past I accept responsibility ... I have advised, I have incited, I have conspired'. It was all the police needed to act. She was arrested 'for procuring and inciting women to commit offences contrary to the Malicious Injuries to Property Act, 1861' and sentenced to three years' penal servitude.

Mrs Pankhurst immediately went on hunger strike, creating a problem for the authorities. Force-feeding the leader of the WSPU was out of the question. But the last thing they wanted was a martyr. Their solution was to rush The Prisoners' (Temporary Discharge for Ill Health) Bill through Parliament, allowing for the release of hunger-strikers so that they might recover, before being returned to prison. It swiftly became known as the 'Cat and Mouse Act', one of the most notorious pieces of suffrage legislation ever passed.

Hoping to capitalise on a tide of anti-militancy feeling in Devon, Bideford NUWSS pushed ahead with its meetings, now under the wing of Mrs and Misses Kelsall. Just two weeks after the destruction of Lloyd George's house, they hosted an 'At Home' in the Station Hall in Westward Ho! Around two hundred people gathered for a debate between Mr Griffiths (for woman suffrage) and Mr Rivington (against). The *Bideford Gazette* reported: 'The Resolution was defeated, but only by five votes, which must be regarded as a great victory in such an anti-suffrage neighbourhood.'

'In such an anti-suffrage neighbourhood.' Much of Torridge remained not only anti-militancy but anti-suffrage, something that was on show when Miss Walford, a NUWSS national organiser, came to speak in Bideford as reported in *The Gazette*:

> A disgraceful scene took place at a Suffrage Meeting in the Town Hall on April 3rd when Mr Cameron Grant and Miss Walford were refused a hearing. After an hour's booing, shouting and singing interrupted by short remarks from the chair, the speakers and the Chairman (The Rev Scholey) retired from the platform. Thereupon three quarters of the audience rushed from the Hall to be ready to receive their visitors in the street. Many of the orderly members of the audience however remained in their seats and someone conceived the idea of asking Mr Cameron Grant to return and give his address. He did so and the motion "that this meeting believes that the extension of the franchise to Women is a measure of Justice and will be for the good of the country" after being seconded by Miss Walford was carried by a large majority. Meantime the crowd outside did their utmost to drown the voices of the speakers within and finally favoured them in the street with a most unwarranted display of hostility before allowing them to drive away.

If it was to make any headway in North Devon, the NUWSS had to get its non-militant message across. In Barnstaple, Christine Wodehouse drafted in some family support. At the beginning of April, an audience gathered at the Parish Church Room to hear two speakers. The first, Mrs Knight-Bruce gave: 'an excellent address from the practical point of view, while Dr Helen Wodehouse carried the subject on to the highest philosophical plane'. Helen Wodehouse, Christine's sister, was well qualified to do this. She achieved a first at Girton and an MA and DPhil at Birmingham before becoming Principal of a new teacher training college at Bingley in Yorkshire.

It was a significant meeting for Christine with membership increasing, particularly among men. Already at the heart of the group were Mr Hired J.P. who took the chair, Mr Abel and Mr Fear, and five new men were recruited at this one meeting. This swelling of the ranks of the non-militant Barnstaple NUWSS can be directly attributed to the increasingly outrageous acts of the militant suffragettes.

Ironically, one of the core perpetrators of the arson campaign was a Devonian. Olive Wharry, then living just outside Holsworthy, was about to make national headlines for an act that many found beyond the pale.

On Wednesday, 19th February 1913 the tea pavilion at Kew Gardens was being redecorated ready for its reopening at Easter. As dusk fell, the tea room was closed with the workmen due to return at 6 o'clock the following morning. All was quiet until 3.15 when one of the night attendants noticed a bright light inside the Pavilion and saw two people running away. *The Guardian* takes up the story:

> Police Constable Hill, who was on duty in the vicinity of Kew Gardens at three o'clock yesterday morning, said he observed the reflections of fire, and on climbing the wall from the roadway saw the two prisoners running across the field of the Richmond Cricket Club. He and a colleague followed, and in the course of the pursuit the prisoners each dropped a portmanteau. When the witness caught the prisoner Lenton [Lilian Lenton was well-known for her involvement in several arson attempts] he said to her, "What are you doing here?' She replied, "I have come to see the fire," and laughed. The witness said, "You will have to come to the station with me," and she replied, "All right; don't touch me." When they got to the gate of the grounds he saw the prisoner Locke [the second woman gave her name as Joyce Locke but was actually Olive Wharry from Holsworthy] place a small pocket

lamp behind the gate post while they were waiting for the gate to be opened... The police officer produced in court one of the portmanteaux and its contents. There were a large saw, a hammer a saw, a bundle or two, strongly redolent of paraffin and some pieces of paper.

Serving the writ at Olive's family home just outside Holsworthy was not straightforward, as the son of the solicitor's clerk recalled:

> My father Stanley J. Rowland, a solicitor's clerk aged 19, was sent in 1913 with a fellow junior clerk named Cowling to serve the writ on Olive Wharry at her home at Whitstone Head, Whitstone, in North Cornwall, near Bude. They cycled out to Whitstone from their employer's office in Holsworthy, about 8 miles, and were admitted by her father Dr Wharry. When they explained their business he refused to let them see his daughter and locked them in his study. After a long while they were released and told to leave, taking the writ with them. As they left one of them flung the writ on the doorstep. This was held to be effective service. Dr Wharry flew into a rage and, calling his servants, chased them off the premises.
>
> Dr Wharry was subsequently prosecuted for assaulting a process server acting in the course of his duties and stood trial at the Old Bailey in London, initially pleading Not Guilty. My father and his colleague were ordered to attend as prosecution witnesses. Neither had been east of Exeter before and it was a great adventure. When they arrived in London they were told that the case would start a day late. The only place in London they had heard of was Madam Tussaud's waxworks and so they spent the day there. In the event Dr Wharry changed his plea to Guilty and their evidence was not required. My father had never before then slept a night away from home. The writ to be served on Miss Wharry related to the arson at Kew but I do not know if it was a civil claim for damages or a criminal summons.
>
> James M. Rowland

The Morning Post of 8th March, 1913, reported the trial:

> At the Central Criminal Court, yesterday, before Mr. Justice Bankes and a jury, Olive Wharry, alias Joyce Lock, twenty-seven, student, was placed on trial charged with having set fire to the Tea Pavilion at the Royal Botanic Gardens, Kew. She pleaded not guilty. Mr. Bodkin ... [prosecuting] said that ... the whole of the Tea Pavilion in Kew Gardens and its contents were destroyed and upon the two women who held the refreshment contract from the Crown a very heavy pecuniary loss had fallen. The contents of the building, which were the property of these two women, were worth £900, [over £70,000 today] but were only insured for £500.

Mr. Justice Bankes, in summing up, said that: 'not very long ago it would have been unthinkable that a well-educated, well-brought-up young woman could have committed a crime like this. Not long ago one would have heard appeals to juries to acquit her on the ground that it was unthinkable she could have committed such a crime. But, unfortunately - and this was all he wanted to say about it - women as a class had forfeited any presumption in their favour of that kind. Unfortunately, they knew that well-educated, well-brought-up women had committed these crimes, and as a consequence it was impossible to approach these cases from the standpoint that they would have approached them from only a few years ago ...'

The jury returned a verdict of guilty. Olive read a long statement denying the jurisdiction of the Court, contending that women should be on the jury, and outlining the case for woman's suffrage:

> Ministers must be warned by the fires in Regent's Park and at Kew lest a worse thing befall them. She was sorry that the two ladies had sustained loss, as she had no grudge against them. At the time she believed that the Pavilion was the property of the Crown, but she wished the two ladies to understand that she was at war, and that in war even non-combatants had to suffer.
>
> The Judge: I have listened to what you have had to say, and my duty is to pass sentence upon you. It is no desire of mine to lecture you, but I am provoked by what you said to day ... The statement you have made seems to me to indicate that you have lost all sense of the consequence of what you are doing. You do not seem to realise the loss and injury and anxiety that such acts as yours cause to all classes - not only to the rich but to the poor and struggling; not only to men but to women. You talk about man-made law as if that was the only law that ought to govern people's actions. You must have heard of another law which says: "Ye shall do unto others as ye would that they should do unto you." That is the law you are breaking. I do not punish you for that. I punish you for the law which is made in consequence of it, and my sentence upon you is that you pay the costs of these proceedings.
>
> Prisoner: I shall refuse to do so. You can do anything you like. I will never pay the costs.
>
> The Judge: My order is that you pay the costs of these proceedings, or that you be imprisoned in the second division for eighteen months.

Prisoner: But I shall not stay in prison.

The Judge: And, in addition, to find two sureties in £100 each that you be of good behaviour and keep the peace for two years from to-day.

Prisoner: Never.

A daily report in Holloway recorded that Olive was taking a little food but it was impossible to say how much. Her weight three weeks into her sentence was 97lbs [44.9 kg or 6 stones 13lbs] but they discovered she had a full hot water bottle under her clothes so her actual weight was 92½lbs, 14lbs less than when she was admitted. The hot water bottle was a tried and tested strategy. In 1911 Vera Holme received a communication from Holloway regarding prisoner number 11636, Evelina Haverfield. It read: 'Will you please forward her hot water bottle on at once.' Given this came via the prison authorities it's surprising that it was still going undetected as a way of disguising weight loss two years later. A doctor's report on Olive Wharry gave more detail:

> I visited this prisoner on March 27th 1913, at HM Prison, Holloway ... I understand that this prisoner has been in prison since March 7th, 1913 and although she gave her word that she would not go on hunger strike if she were allowed to remain in a certain part of the prison, there is little doubt that she is surreptitiously getting rid of her food; in fact, I understand that last evening she was observed through the cell inspection hole to tie up several small packets and put them in her jersey and when searched, these were found to contain food. The prisoner admitted to me that she had done this, but added that she considered that she was taking sufficient nourishment. She refused to allow me to examine her, or to be weighed; she would not even let me feel her pulse. Nevertheless, it is very clear that she has seriously reduced her bodily health, in fact, the last time she had been weighed shewed that she lost 7½ lbs. in the week. She is a very frail person with a very defective circulation. Her hands are cold and very blue, the

pupils are widely dilated. She will not permit anyone to remain with her during meal times and says that if she is watched, she will go on hunger strike.

She may take more food; on the other hand, if she continues to become more emaciated, or shows more marked signs of inanition [lack of energy] or exhaustion, I am of opinion that the question of forcible feeding will have to be seriously considered, and as far as one can at present observe, I do not regard her to be a good subject, at the moment, for such feeding. Maurice Craig M.D. FRCP

Olive Wharry was released under the Cat and Mouse Act just over a month later having been on hunger strike for thirty-two days, apparently without the prison authorities noticing. Her usual weight was 7st 11lbs; when released she weighed 5st 9lbs. This demonstrates a staggering commitment to the cause. She was prepared to go to any lengths to conceal her weight loss, a potentially fatal path.

Lilian Lenton, Olive's co-conspirator, remained defiant. Some years later in a radio interview she boasted: 'Whenever I was out of prison my object was to burn two buildings a week... The object was to create an absolutely impossible condition of affairs in the country, to prove it was impossible to govern without the consent of the governed.' It was a stance approved by the WSPU leadership. When interviewed by the press, Flora Drummond repeated that incidents such as the burning of Lloyd George's house showed the determination of the women. 'It is an example of how far they will go and we are proud of such women.' Sylvia Pankhust recalled this escalation of violence:

> The brief truce before the withdrawal of the Reform Bill and its amendments, was followed by destructive militancy on a hitherto unparalleled scale ... Boat-houses and sports pavilions in England, Ireland and Scotland, and a grand-stand at Ayr race-course were burnt down. Mrs. Cohen, a Leeds member of the deputation to Lloyd George, broke the glass of a jewel-case in the Tower of London. Works of art and objects of exceptional value became the target of determined militants. Thirteen pictures were hacked in the Manchester Art Gallery. Refreshment pavilions were burnt down in Regent's Park and Kew Gardens, where the glass in three orchid houses was smashed, and the plants, thus exposed, were broken and torn up by the roots. Empty houses and other unattended buildings were systematically sought out and set on fire, and many were destroyed ... Hugh Franklin set fire to an empty railway carriage; he was imprisoned and forcibly fed. An old cannon was fired near Dudley Castle, shattering glass and terrifying the neighbourhood. Bombs were placed near the Bank of England, at Wheatley Hall, Doncaster, at Oxted Station, and on the steps of a Dublin Insurance Office. Lloyd George's new house in process of erection at Walton-on-the-Hill was injured beyond repair by a bomb explosion.

It was a strategy that brought the suffragettes a deluge of publicity, not always the kind they hoped for. Adverse press coverage fired up the Ilfracombe group to retaliate with two letters to the Gazette simply signed 'Another tax resister,' and 'A tax-paying English woman.' The second is headed:

> MILITANT SUFFRAGETTES
>
> Dear Sir - The Press has lately been much concerned with certain attacks on property by certain women. With great unction the papers have gloated over harrowing details of suffrage arsenals, of arson or ruined golf greens and have shed tear after tear of

> printers ink in recording the doleful deeds of the "Wild Women". Visions of universal anarchy in which howling female fiends predominate, rise to the minds of the trembling readers as the future probably in store for this unhappy country. Now, sir, we have been so consistently fed with this same highly spiced food, that we are a little satiated with it. What about change? Suppose your interesting paper leads the way, and gives us a weekly diet of some of the reasons and happenings which have gradually driven women into a violence which they hate.

The writer cites the shameful fiasco regarding the women's amendments to the Reform Bill and pours scorn on Cabinet Ministers' promises and their lack of progress protesting on strictly constitutional lines. She continues:

> Secondly, I suggest that instead of somewhat highly coloured accounts of the "Wild Women's" doings, the press should make a few plain straight-forward and truthful remarks as to the violent, outrageous and indecent assaults by men on women at various deputations, political and suffrage meetings ... These little failings of the male sex, however, the Press usually pass over.

Now if she's speaking in the street,
Or any other place,
Bring up your eggs, or clods of turf,
And hit her in the face.
March up, brave boys! By hundreds charge,
Upset her on the ground!
Then sit upon her head and twist
Her elbow gently round.
March in from all your clubs and pubs
And toot your motor horn,
For new sport came to Englishmen
When Suffragettes were born.

I suggest that when women's attacks upon property receive attention, a little of the limelight should turn on men's attacks on their persons.

Thirdly I suggest that the Press, instead of inciting hooligans to an ever greater hooliganism than nature originally endowed them with, and instead of helping to bar and shut the door against women, should endeavour seriously to find the remedy for these distracting events. As it is remarkably simple, and as only one exists, it seems extraordinary to us simply-minded women that there should be any difficulty about it. Give us the Vote, that is all ...

Could anything be more beautifully simple? Why then does the Press not submit that simple remedy to the British public with the same lavish and overflowing generosity with which it submits statements intended to do harm to the women's cause? We cannot admit that the enlightened pressmen of to-day are ignorant; it is unthinkable. We cannot think they are prejudiced: it is unbelievable. We cannot persuade ourselves they are afraid of a few women putting a cross on a ballot paper; it is incredible. The only thing to suppose is that it simply hasn't occurred to them that the thing could be settled so easily. Perhaps, Sir, you will lead the way to the enlightenment of your fellow editors on this point and by so doing earn the gratitude of the women who want freedom, and the men who want peace.

This forthright letter, written by Marie Newby, Anne Ball or Margaret Eldridge - or perhaps composed jointly - oozes with frustration at men's inability to grasp the obvious solution; a frustration that was soon to thrust North Devon into the spotlight.

Chapter Seventeen
Countdown to Militancy
April into May 1913

In the spring of 1913, the Ilfracombe suffragettes raised their profile, renting a shop at 2, High Street to exhibit WSPU posters. They decorated the walls with banners declaring 'God defend us for our cause is just', 'Votes for Women' and 'Great is Truth and will Prevail'. The space was also perfect for launching weekly debates but the local paper did them no favours. Instead of focusing on the crucial issues in their first debate the *Ilfracombe Gazette* chose to run with the perverse headline, *Miss Ball on Narrow-Chested Young Men*. The actual topics discussed were rather different.

Despite - or perhaps because of - the paper's spoiling tactics, a good crowd of around fifty men and women turned out for the first debate. Some names stand out:

THE PRIME MOVERS

Those for Woman Suffrage:

Mr Day, Mr Pickett Junr, Mr Kelly

Miss Ball, Mrs Newby, Miss Eldridge, Miss Ross

Those for, but against militancy:

Mr Matthews, Mr Trengrove

Those against:

Mr Blackmore, Mr Stephens, Mr Bryant, Mr Trelease

According to the Gazette, Mr Day takes the bull by the horns and opens with a plea to the audience to separate the tactics being used from the principle behind them. 'Women have taken their share in the building up of this great nation ... They have stood shoulder to shoulder with men, and little by little this great nation has been built up ... The argument was used that men were superior to women ...'

'Very few,' says a lady.

'In some respects,' says Mr Day, 'I am inclined to agree that the greatest artists, authors and musicians were men.'

'No,' protests a chorus of female voices.

'There are spheres of life,' Mr Day hastily continues, 'in which women are superior. Think you,' he adds in conclusion, 'that some of the men in Ilfracombe who will sell their votes for a pint of beer are more capable of exercising the vote than you who have come here tonight to earnestly and thoughtfully consider this theme.' (Applause)

Anne Ball - 'The first thing thrown at us - very often by narrow-chested young men - is that women cannot fight and therefore should not have the vote. I know a good many farmers' wives and domestics who would put up a much better fight than a good many men I know. They said that women who could not fight shouldn't have the vote but what about blind and deaf men and others who could not fight? They still have the vote. The next stock argument is that woman's place is in the home. But what about the five million women who have no place they can call their own, but who have to go out and earn their living?

'The last argument,' she continues,' is a glorious one. They say we are deficient in intellect.' (Loud laughter from the women) 'I admit there are greater authors, artists, and musicians among men. These men are geniuses, and the last idea of a genius is that it is a form of degeneracy (Laughter) ... women have not had the chance to use their brains as men have ... but women are all-round people.'

Mr Matthews - 'I am unable to understand why women should be allowed to vote in a local Council election and not in a Parliamentary election ... but I am of the opinion that the militants have retarded the movement rather than advanced it. They have no right to destroy property and to endanger human life ... but I believe it is a right and just cause, and that it will ultimately triumph.'

Marie Newby - 'Women have spent years trying to obtain the vote by peaceful means and one of the largest petitions ever presented to the House of Commons was in favour of woman suffrage.'

She is constantly interrupted by a young man in the audience, but it's a different matter when the Chairman eventually asks him to stand and champion the opponents of woman suffrage. 'I did not come here to make a speech,' he says.

Margaret Eldridge - appeals to Liberals. 'It is a Liberal principle that there should be no taxation without representation, but what have we done that they do not trust us?'

Mr Blackmore - advances one of the most vociferous arguments against giving votes to women. 'The women might rush the country into war, but men have to be in the firing line. They were bound to rely on muscle. It was a significant fact that the Saviour of mankind was a man.'

'And the Blessed Virgin was a woman,' a voice in the audience parries.

The debate continues back and forth with Anne Ball and Margaret Eldridge fielding most of the objections. But one comment from Mr Stephens must have left them speechless. 'It is not women who want the vote, but something between the masculine and the feminine.' It was left to the retiring young man to get them back on course, suggesting that as men had to earn all the money they should say how it was spent.

Mr Day - 'Even a married woman who works at her own home in providing meals and looking after the children earns as well as her husband, and therefore is equally entitled to a vote.' His comment brings the Gazette's report of the first debate to a close. A resolution in favour of woman suffrage is carried with one dissenter.

The second debate a week later is a very different affair with heckling from the anonymous young man replaced by the outspoken views of several anti-suffragettes. A report in the Ilfracombe Gazette again allows us to dip in and out of the debate:

Mr E. Stephens - 'The militants have no men to take them in their arms and therefore they have to go to the policeman ... women are not physically fitted to sit in the House of Commons, as it needs a strong physique to stand the strain ... ... The natives of our Indian possessions would not be loyal if they knew that England was governed by women ... To give votes to women would mean breaking up home life, which is the greatest asset this country has ever had ... Why was their agitation only started when the Liberals came into office? Because it is financed by the Conservatives (Laughter) ... Female prisoners were treated better than male prisoners, and did policemen handle women as roughly as they did men?'

Voices chorus - 'Yes.'

Mr R. Pickett Jun. - 'I take exception to Mr Stephen's remarks about the suffragettes being subsidised by the Conservatives ... They do publish a balance sheet, which is more than can be said about other political parties ... The women were above board, and that was one of the great things they want in politics to-day. The vote has been a potent instrument in the uplifting of the working men of this country. Take the railway strike. If the men had not been represented in Parliament, the Government would have taken no notice of them. I cannot see how women's position in this country will be improved unless they have the vote.'

Mr Stephens - 'The noisy voice of a few should not be taken as the voice of the women of this country.'

Mr Blackmore - 'No adequate reason has been advanced why women should have the vote. Show us that this drastic change you ask us to make will be beneficial to the nation at large ... Women get more consideration than they could ever expect from their own sex.'

Shouts of 'No' from the ladies.

Mr Blackmore - 'At the last meeting a lady said that one of the largest petitions ever presented to Parliament was in favour of woman suffrage, but petitions were simply treated as waste paper, and rightly so. There was no proof by example that the granting of votes to women had benefited any nation or state ... your citizenship is as real as that of a man, your service to the state is as vital as that of men, but you are differently constituted beings. You have talents that are not identical with men's, but complementary. This country must be guided by the steady hand of man.' (Loud laughter from the women) Mr Blackmore concluded he was willing to support woman suffrage if they could convince him that the result of giving votes to women would mean better Government.

Anne Ball - 'After hearing the previous speakers I must apologise for my very existence on the face of the earth. The last speaker confessed that petitions were of no use. As long as the women endeavoured to make themselves heard by constitutional methods they could not succeed, and therefore they had to become militants. I agree there are differences between the sexes, but it is those differences we want legislated for. At present we are under a male Government solely. The judges and juries in the law courts are all men. I should like men to imagine themselves being tried by female judges and jury and to have all men turned out of court while the case was being heard.

'An MP was telling his son how he should deal with correspondents. "Letters from voters should be attended to at once, and after these the letters from potential voters, but letters from women could be torn up and thrown in the waste-paper basket." If the Government had something to get from women in the shape of the vote, the women would soon have their grievance redressed. One speaker said that to give women the vote should be to break up home life. If I had a husband, would he like me less because I voted once in four or five years? Would it tend to domestic happiness if John said to Mary, "You must have no opinion of your own." That will not do. Physical force is not the only power in the revolution of the world, as some would have them believe. It was said, too, that there were greater artists, authors, etc among men than among women, but women have been engaged in rearing the race, which is a much nobler work than painting pictures.'

Mr Day - 'I cannot understand why a lady of Miss Ball's intelligence should not have the vote. And taxation and representation should go together. Not only the rich but every man and woman in the state have to pay taxation. I cannot understand how any man with progressive thought opposed woman suffrage. It was said that women did not want the vote. When it was proposed to give farm labourers the vote the same thing was argued, but as the late W.E.Gladstone said, "If there is one farm labourer in this country who has educated himself and wants the vote I am not going to withhold it from that one because others are foolish enough not to want it." If only ten per cent of the women wanted the vote they should not withhold it from them. I believe most of the opposition is simply prejudice.

'As to the militant suffragettes, it is the only way they have of expressing their feelings and forcing themselves on the attention of the government. The time was bound to come when women would have the vote, and when it did come they would be surprised that they had ever opposed it. The women's cause is bound to prosper because of their fidelity, loyalty and tenacity.'

Mr Stephens - 'Thirty years ago I was in favour of Women Suffrage, but I had no idea then that women would make such fools of themselves. If anything has done harm to the movement it is militancy, which is one of the greatest curses seen in our land. When women will get the vote now I do not know.'

Mr Bryant - 'Most suffragettes are out to get the vote for the rich women only. If there is any section of the community that needs protection it is certainly the weak: the rich have power in their wealth. The people who do not know where the money for the next day's food is coming from are the ones who deserve and ought to have the vote. Are the ladies present who have servants willing that the cook should have the vote?'

'Yes,' say the ladies emphatically.

Mr Bryant - 'I am very pleased that so many ladies have so comprehensive a view of the subject. But when you read that at Bideford the Vicar of Appledore ... instanced the people who deserved the vote as Mrs Hamlyn of Clovelly Court, it makes us very suspicious of the motive behind it all. They must not have any half measures. All women must have the vote. If one section only gets the vote - the rich section - they would never consent to the poor women getting it. You can take it from me,' he adds, 'that the rich people will try to stop the poor women from having the vote.'

Marie Newby - 'The Suffrage Societies demand that all women should have the vote. The Women's Social and Political Union would not accept the conciliation basis, including simply women householders. But the objections keep coming.'

Mr Trengrove - 'I condemn the abominable practice of destroying letters, and the burning of buildings which deprive innocent people of their means of livelihood. Until they (the suffragettes) stop militancy they will never get the Vote.'

Week three brings the third and final debate, and there is no doubt about the Gazette's focus:

MILITANTS TACTICS

ILFRACOMBE SUFFRAGETTES ATTITUDE

About a dozen ladies voted in favour of militancy at the third debate on Woman Suffrage held at the room of the Ilfracombe Suffrage society, 2 Church St, on Friday evening last.

Mr Matthews - in the chair. 'Since coming to years of discretion I have been in favour of votes for women. I contend that men secured the vote in much the same way as women are endeavouring to do so today. The men had to fight for the privileges they enjoy today. The question of Votes for Women is one of humanity. Men are looked upon by some as lords of creation, but all are of one blood, all are human, and all should enjoy the same privileges. If women have to pay taxes they should have a voice in the management of affairs.'

A male voice - 'They do.'

Mr Matthews - 'I do not approve of the tactics of the militants, by whom the movement has been retarded. But in one way it could be put a stop to, and that is by giving women the vote.'

Miss Eldridge - 'For a long time no legislation has been passed for women except to coerce them; that is because they have no vote behind them. A single gentleman who spoke to you last time evidently thinks that the suffrage agitation is carried on only by disappointed spinsters. Of course we know a lady has never refused an offer of marriage since the world began. (Laughter) I really wonder that the gentleman who spoke to you last week does venture out of doors in Leap Year, seeing there are so many widows and spinsters about that might be waylaying him at every turn (More laughter) It is difficult to please some people.

'If we disappointed ones stay at home and nurse our tabby cats you speak of wasted lives. If we venture out of doors then woman's place is the home. Surely we may come abroad to do a little good in the world if it is only to cry "Votes for Women". I quite agree that the place of many women is in the home but are all the nurses, shop girls, waitresses and servants to retire to their homes and stay there?

'In New Zealand and Australia the number of men is greater than that of women. Yet the women have had the vote there since 1893 ... they did not expect the vote to do everything but it was the bulwark of a woman's freedom, the starting point of future progress and without her free assistance, the evolution of the world would be grievously hindered.

'Another speaker has referred to woman's inferior strength. There are two kinds of strength, that of the battering ram and that of the watch spring, both equally useful in different ways. It is not a question of rival strengths. A horse has greater strength than a man, but you cannot give it therefore greater rights. It was said that some could not fight but they had certainly been doing something in that line lately. (Laughter) It had been said that Mrs Pankhurst would have been quite equal to organising the South African War. I trust we are passing away from the age of combat, but a woman could fight to-day if really necessary, they are splendid rifle shots and riders. War today is so scientific that little of the old muscular strength is required; it is all brain, nerve and science.

'All the Kings and statesmen love to see the peoples they have trained able to become self-governing. The best of our men have taught us to love freedom, open dealing, and to hate crooked ways. You can do no less than give us your help, even at cost to yourselves, to help us to gain our political freedom, and to gain our footing in the new world that is opening to us all, and in the new order that we trust is dawning, when person counts for more than property, when a person guilty of injury to a child will be more severely punished than a suffragette who breaks a window. The call to compare criminal sentences has been very insistent of late and many gross inequalities have been exposed.' (Applause)

Mr Matthews - 'If you vote for Woman Suffrage you vote in favour of militant methods.'

Cries from the audience - 'No, No.'

Mr Stephens - 'If women are granted the franchise the country will be thrown into turmoil. To go smashing up things in the manner the militants had done was without sense or reason.'

Mr Kelly - 'I must compliment Miss Eldridge on her excellent speech. I may say that I am absolutely in favour of votes for women (Hear, hear and applause) I cannot see why there should be the least possible objection to it. If the great party in power to-day had thought it was in their interest to give votes to women it would have been granted before now.

'When Sir Stafford Northcote spoke here some years ago he addressed his audience as 'men and women,' and said, 'what do you want better than woman.' (Loud laughter) At the present time women can vote for councillors, why should they not vote for Members of Parliament? We hear a lot about the militants, but what have the men done to get the vote? We have only got to look back to past history. When men wanted cheaper bread they smashed windows with stones. What were they?'

From the audience - 'Men.'

Mr Kelly - 'And women are women. Men have shown the women what to do.'

From the audience - 'Are you supporting militancy?'

Mr Kelly - 'I am not supporting it but women should have the same freedom that men enjoy.'

The meeting ended with a resolution expressing disapproval of militant tactics. It was close. The show of hands in agreement with the motion was expected. Not so anticipated was the number of hands raised against, and therefore supporting militancy. A few at first, then more until, to the astonishment of some, they easily equalled the first vote. More than a dozen Ilfracombe women voted in favour of militancy.

Chapter Eighteen
The Ultimate Protest
Early summer 1913

Militancy wasn't going away. Residents of Ilfracombe flicking through their copy of the Gazette a few days later were greeted by the headline:

MANSION DESTROYED
MILITANTS CAMPAIGN OF OUTRAGE

> Militant suffragists are blamed for a number of outrages which were committed during the weekend. On Saturday morning Farington Hall, a mansion near Dundee, the residence of Mr Henry McGrady, a former Lord Provost of the city, was destroyed by fire ... Later in the day the Chief Constable in the city received

a copy of the *Suffragette* declaring: "Farington Hall: A protest against British tyranny. Blame Asquith and company. A significant demand for redress of a grievance from the outclassed."

New members continued to join the Ilfracombe group, just in time to hear a significant speaker in the militant campaign, Mr Charles Gray.

Charles Gray was a key member of the Men's Political Union, founded in 1909 as a militant organisation for male suffragists, even adopting the WSPU colours to show their support. A notice in the Ilfracombe Gazette announced: 'This will be the first time that a representative of one of the men's unions has spoken in Ilfracombe. It may not be generally known that there are several men's societies to which many well-known men who believe in the justice of Votes for Women belong.'

The Honorary Treasurer of the Men's Union was a familiar face - it was Mr Harben, the previous candidate for the Barnstaple division who resigned in protest at the force-feeding of women in Holloway. Ilfracombe WSPU had recently sent a gold-mounted walking stick to him as a mark of their esteem and gratitude for his principled stand.

Mr Pickett Jnr left the audience in no doubt of his support for the cause. 'As a result of the actions of Mrs Pankhurst, the question of Woman Suffrage has become a practical one. Women have acted rightly in forcing the matter to the front. I am a Liberal but cannot understand why any Liberal should refuse to give votes to women. It's all very well to stand on political platforms and preach the doctrine of equality, but they should be prepared to give the rights they enjoy to other people as well.

'Women are more and more becoming wage earners. All admit that the vote is a potent weapon for bettering industrial conditions. If the social and economic conditions of women were bettered, it would have a beneficial effect on the social and economic conditions of the male workers of this country. If for that reason only, I support the demand of the women for the vote.' (Applause)

Charles Gray went further. 'I am a Liberal too, and for that reason I cannot support the present Government. Men have no right to deny women the vote. Some women are infinitely superior to some men who exercise the vote.'

'Hear, hear,' - an emphatic call from a lady in the hall.

Charles Gray - 'In today's papers there is an account of a woman who has been appointed a Justice of the Peace. Part of her duties will be to certify whether men are sane or insane. If she said a man was insane he would be denied the right to vote. It's absurd that she can do this, but is not allowed to vote herself ... Instead of trying to crush the movement, the Government should see there is a wrong, and a reason for the discontent. If the Government had been more statesmanlike they would have looked further into the question; they would have seen that militant methods would never have been taken up by women if there had not been real and fundamental reasons beneath.

'Regarding the abomination of forced feeding, the suffragettes have gone on hunger strike because the government refuses to recognise them as political offenders. Forcible feeding is simply a method to crush the spirit out of the women. The government cannot find another way out of the difficulty and so they torture the women.'

Less than a month later, another Men's Society was represented in Ilfracombe at a meeting organised by the Church League for Women's Suffrage. Lieut. John Leonard Cather was the Honorary Secretary of the Men's Society for Women's Rights, and someone who made his views plain at the time of the census. He refused to complete details of the women in his house while they had no voice.

Invitations to the meeting were issued by the Church League organiser who just happened to be - Marie Newby, now actively campaigning in more than one organisation. A good crowd gathered at the Osborne Hotel to hear Lieut. and Mrs Cather speak. It was a reunion for the ladies. Joan Cather was an active suffragette who had also taken part in the March 4th protest and been imprisoned alongside Marie.

Their presence may have caused some tension with the Chair for the meeting, the Rev McMichael, Vicar of Lee. The Gazette reported, 'In opening the proceedings the chairman referred to militancy which he deplored, for it was keeping the cause back. He appealed to all Church people to endeavour to stop it.'

Just two weeks later the talk was of much more than broken windows. Someone who had also been in Holloway at the same time as Marie and Joan Cather was Emily Wilding Davison. The next news they heard of her, described here by Emmeline Pankhurst, was devastating:

> Emily Wilding Davison, who had been associated with the militant movement since 1906, gave up her life for the women's cause by throwing herself in the path of the thing, next to property, held most sacred to Englishmen - sport. Miss Davison went to the races at Epsom, and breaking through the barriers which separated the vast crowds from the race course, rushed in the path of the galloping horses and caught the bridle of the King's horse, which was leading all the others. The horse fell, throwing his jockey and crushing Miss Davison in such shocking fashion that she was carried from the course in a dying condition.

Everything possible was done to save her life. The great surgeon, Mr. Mansell Moullin, put everything aside and devoted himself to her case, but though he operated most skilfully, the injuries she had received were so frightful that she died four days later without once having recovered consciousness. Members of the Union were beside her when she breathed her last, on June 8th, and on June 14th they gave her a great public funeral in London. Crowds lined the streets as the funeral car, followed by thousands of women, passed slowly and sadly to St. George's Church, Bloomsbury, where the memorial services were held.

Emily Wilding Davison was a B. A. of London University, and had taken first class honours at Oxford in English Language and Literature. Yet the women's cause made such an appeal to her reason and her sympathies that she put every intellectual and social appeal aside and devoted herself untiringly and fearlessly to the work of the Union. She had suffered many imprisonments, had been forcibly fed and most brutally treated.

On one occasion when she had barricaded her cell against the prison doctors, a hose pipe was turned on her from the window and she was drenched and all but drowned in the icy water while workmen were breaking down her cell door. Miss Davison, after this experience, expressed to several of her friends the deep conviction that now, as in days called uncivilised, the conscience of the people would awaken only to the sacrifice of a human life.

At one time in prison she tried to kill herself by throwing herself head-long from one of the upper galleries, but she succeeded only in sustaining cruel injuries. Ever after that time she clung to her conviction that one great tragedy, the deliberate throwing into the breach of a human life, would put an end to the intolerable torture of women. And so she threw herself at the King's horse, in full view of the King and Queen and a great multitude of their Majesties' subjects, offering up her life as a petition to the King, praying for the release of suffering women throughout England and the world. No one can possibly doubt

> that that prayer can forever remain unanswered, for she took it straight to the Throne of the King of all the worlds.

Whether Emily 'offered up her life' is still open to question, given that she had a return train ticket in her pocket. But whatever the motive, her death both rocked and galvanised the movement. In Ilfracombe, the decision was made to send a cross of flowers in WSPU colours to the funeral, before welcoming the many new members who joined after the tragedy.

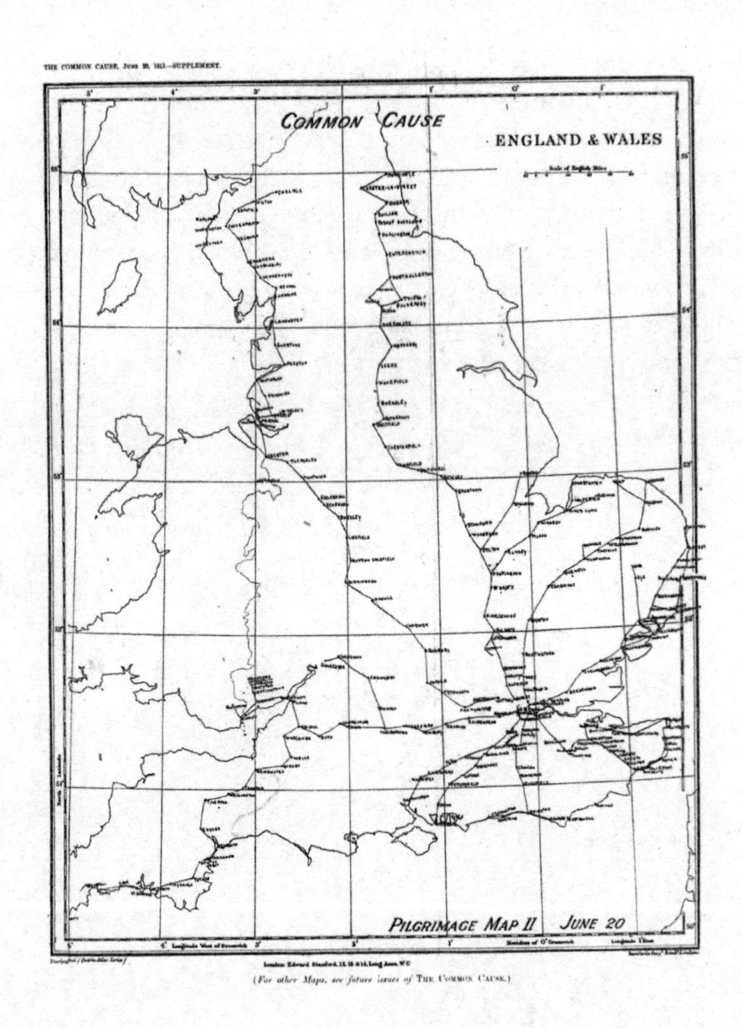

Chapter Nineteen
Devon Pilgrims
Summer 1913

While the country reeled from the death of Emily Davison, the NUWSS pursued their campaign step by step, literally, through the West Country. They were planning a Great Pilgrimage to London to publicise the suffrage cause. It was part of their new policy to educate and inform. Plymouth organiser, Dr Mabel Ramsay, explained: 'It is the conviction of every National Unionist that the Suffrage cause has all to gain and nothing to lose by the education of the public, not only on Suffrage itself, but on all questions of pubic interest.' But she recognised it would be a long haul. 'It is evidently becoming a question of persistence whether we win the vote at once or not. Politicians always hope they can wear down the patience and enthusiasm of those who clamour for reform ... But the least sign of discouragement on our part puts fresh heart into our opponents, and we must see to it that no such encouragement is given.'

In contrast to the militant tactics of the WSPU, the NUWSS was more resigned to setbacks along the way. 'Suffragists have seen their cause temporarily defeated in the House of Commons through the failure of a Prime Minister to honour his pledges, but they are working in the constituencies with undiminished courage and hopefulness.' That hopefulness was evident in Bideford where Miss Walford bravely returned to offer a series of lectures on the subject of, 'How legislation affects the woman in the home.' She was supported by Miss Baretti, who, as reported in the *Bideford Gazette*, tackled the anti-suffragists head-on:

> Anti-suffragists used as one of their arguments the fact that nearly all the great work of the world - railways, navigation, building etc - was done by men but they did not always add that it was the men's womenkind who set them free for the work by doing the double share of the daily work necessary for the maintenance of life.
>
> Innovations were always regarded at first, by the majority of people, with distrust. Umbrellas even were pronounced impious by some people, the first man who carried an open umbrella in Baltimore being mobbed by little boys. When women first began to ride bicycles there was an arrant cry against it: people said it was unwomanly and counter to nature for women to ride and that women had no nerve and it would be dangerous for them in

traffic. However, women insisted and now everyone had accepted it. Suffragists hoped it would be the same with the vote; ten years after it was granted it would seem the natural thing for women to go to the poll with the men.

A vote was not an inherently masculine thing - men were not born with votes! And that being the case it seemed hard that when women had attained the qualifications that give men a vote, they should be refused it. At one time the power to vote was confined to the rich and the great in the land and then precisely the same arguments were used against the extension of the franchise among men as are now used against extending it to women.

Power has always hated to share itself with others. There were certain great injustices in the laws of England that one would like to get altered; for instance, that a woman is not recognised as the parent of her child. She knew one woman whose child had been vaccinated against her wishes and those of her husband because the latter was at sea, and the woman was refused a certificate of exemption, being unable to prove to the Magistrate that she was acting as her husband's agent in asking for it, and her own opposing to vaccination went for nothing, she not being the legal parent at all ...

> She acknowledged that women could get their wishes dealt with eventually without the vote, but only very eventually and only by means of a tremendous amount of work, vast organisation, mass meetings and so forth.

Miss Walford's appearance was followed by a debate in the Public Rooms between Mrs Gladstone Solomon, for the anti's, and Miss Geraldine Cooke, championing the suffrage cause. It was a lively exchange delivered to a packed audience of over 500 but ending with a defeat for Miss Cooke.

Despite this setback the NUWSS continued to thrive in North Devon, consolidating their links with the national movement. At the next meeting in Barnstaple, all the talk was of the West Country's part in the Great Pilgrimage. This one meeting alone raised £2 9s towards costs - the equivalent of almost £300 today.

With contributions like this from groups across the country, the organisation was complete and on June 18th 1913, seven women set out from Land's End. They attracted enormous crowds as they progressed through Cornwall into Devon. The *Common Cause* reported: 'Results so far have more than justified the enterprise ... Extraordinary amount of interest been shown by the public ... In every important town the audiences can be reckoned in four figures ... An enormous amount of propaganda been accomplished. Eighty dozen *Common Causes* sold so far. The Pilgrims are accompanied by a large covered van with its head-board painted, "Land's End to London" and the red, white and green lettering on its tilt describing the National Union and its methods. Through the length of Cornwall there is a new understanding of the meaning of the suffrage movement, and thousands now recognise the significance of the Constitutional red, white and green.' The colours were displayed on a shoulder sash and marchers were encouraged to wear a raffia cockle shell, the traditional symbol of pilgrimage, pinned to their hats.

After speaking to an enormous crowd of around 1,500 gathered at Looe, the pilgrims moved on to a rousing reception at

Plymouth Corn Exchange where they were welcomed by Dr Mabel Ramsay. It was an emotional reunion. Someone who made the entire pilgrimage, part walking, part travelling in the van, was her mother, Annie Ramsay, then in her sixties. 'Annie, bottle of sal volatile in her bag, stayed the course with Miss Baly of Exeter, both of whom started from Land's End. Dr Mabel Ramsay marched to Taunton then returned, unable to stay away from her practice as a medical practitioner.'

On July 1st the Pilgrimage was warmly received at Totnes. The following day they moved on, with some trepidation, to their next stop, Newton Abbot. The *Common Cause* reports: 'Here Mr Murren took the chair and we had a crowded but most orderly meeting of some 3,000 persons. The undisturbed hearing accorded to our speakers was a surprise to everyone for Newton Abbot is notorious for turbulent meetings, and it had been freely professed that we should have disorder.' They were thinking of the treatment Mrs Pankhurst received when campaigning against the Liberal candidate there in 1908. But the Devon lap actually saw very little disorder apparently due, according to the *Common Cause*, to the: 'less excitable nature of the people (compared to Cornwall)! … Also, the police protected us with special care and have shown admirable firmness in their handling of the crowds.'

On the 4th the Pilgrims left Teignmouth to hold meetings at Dawlish and Starcross and then crossed by ferry to Exmouth. On Saturday 5th, they marched towards Exeter. It was a significant moment. The Exeter Society had organised a great demonstration. About 300 suffragists marched in procession through the streets: 'providing a most picturesque spectacle with their gallant show of banners. At the end of the procession a monster meeting was held at the bottom of Paris Street, where some six or seven thousand people assembled.' Even at the more conservative end of the estimate, a crowd of six thousand spectators was a spectacular achievement.

The following morning the Pilgrimage moved on to Tiverton, Wellington and Taunton. At times along the way some spectators confused the Pilgrims with militants. One man who allowed them to rest in his orchard facetiously remarked: 'You may burn the nettles, but please leave me my apple trees.' The Ladies continued to attract large crowds as they made their way through Somerset, stopping to hold rallies at Bridgwater, Street and in the natural amphitheatre halfway up Cheddar Gorge.

They joined pilgrims from Bristol, Bath, Gloucester, Swindon and all places in between until finally massing in Hyde Park, contributing to the estimated crowd of 50,000 women who had marched from all corners of the country. And it was Annie Ramsay who stood to remind the crowds of their message: "The Women of the West Demand Votes for Women."

Chapter Twenty
The Flames of Injustice in Lynton
July into August 1913

While the NUWSS marched, Ilfracombe WSPU was consolidating its position with an influx of new members in the wake of the death of Emily Wilding Davison. The group they joined had fundamentally changed. The public vote in favour of militancy had forged a new sense of purpose and they lost no time in making plans. Their first move was to harness the support of someone well qualified to support them - WSPU organiser, Mary Phillips. She was a core activist, even pressing Christabel for permission to take part in more militant activity as far back as 1909. But it was WSPU policy for organisers to stay out of trouble, leaving travelling militants such as Lilian Lenton and Kitty Marion to take on the more dangerous criminal acts. Permission was refused. Mary obeyed for the next three years but significantly, just before her visit to Ilfracombe,

Christabel dismissed her, claiming she was ineffective as a district organiser. Whatever the truth of it, Mary was now free to act on her militant tendencies.

Mary was familiar to the group as one of the 'Exeter Hunger Strikers', but this was the first time they had met. On behalf of all members, old and new, Marie welcomed Mary to Ilfracombe to speak on the sole topic - militancy. Mary reassured waverers that the responsibility for it lay entirely with a government that had turned a deaf ear to argument and reason. It had, she said, treated the question in Parliament with discreditable tricks and evasions, refusing time for Suffrage Bills to become law even after they had secured large majorities on their second reading. It had imprisoned and tortured women when they protested, even using the mild militancy of the early days of the WSPU.

It was a well-received message, one that Mary later repeated to the immense Ilfracombe crowd that gathered to hear her. While she spoke, the local group worked the crowd, selling papers and recruiting even more members. It was all part of a relentless campaign to expand their ranks with members committed to militancy - a momentum that could have only one outcome.

The core members of the Ilfracombe group began to put together a plan that would bring the controversial tactics of the militant suffragettes much closer to home. Their focus for that plan lay in Lynton, a few miles east of Ilfracombe along the North Devon coast. Sir Albert De Rutzen, chief magistrate at Bow Street Court and father-in-law of Frank Newnes, the current owner of Hollerday House in Lynton, was about to find out exactly how the hundreds of suffragettes he had condemned to the hardship of Holloway felt about his actions.

Hollerday House couldn't have been a more perfect target. Valuable, with impeccable credentials ... and empty. It was WSPU policy for a small band of trained militants to carry out high profile acts to protect local activists. Two candidates for the events about to unfold in Lynton were Olive Wharry from Holsworthy and her partner in crime at Kew, Lilian Lenton. But Olive was in prison and Lilian in hiding, facing re-arrest. This left the name immediately beneath Lilian on the list of suffragists under the Cat and Mouse Act - Kitty Marion, a known arsonist.

SUFFRAGISTS UNDER THE CAT AND MOUSE ACT

Name.	Sentenced.	Released.	Re-arrested.
Mrs. Pankhurst	April 3	(1) April 12	May 26
		(2) May 30	June 14
		(3) June 16	July 21
Miss Kenney	June 17	(1) June 21	July 2
		(2) July 5	July 14
		(3) July 18	—
Miss Kerr	"	June 25	—
Mrs. Sanders	"	(1) June 23	July 9
		(2) July 11	—
Miss Barrett	"	(1) June 21	July 2
		(2) July 5	July 17
		(3) July 21	—
Miss Lake	"	June 21	July 2
Miss Lennox	"	(1) "	June 29
		(2) July 3	—
Mr. Clayton	"	June 23	Missing
Mrs. Shaw	June 21	June 27	"
Mrs. Palmer (Irish)	May 26	June 18	—
Mrs. Ryan "	"	"	—
Miss Walsh "	"	"	—
Miss Thomson (Scotch)	May 19	May 23	Missing
Miss A. Scott "	"	(1) May 24	June 12
		(2) June 16	Missing
Miss Hudson "	"	May 25	"
Mr. Franklin	March 8	April 28	"
Miss Stevenson	March 5	April 29	"
Miss Brady	April 12	"	"
Miss Dean	"	"	"
*Mrs. Baines	May 5	(1) May 12	July 10
		(2) July 20	—
Miss Lenton	Com. for trial, June 9	June 17	Missing
†Miss Marion	July 3	(1) July 8	July 12
		(2) July 17	—
Miss Giveen	"	July 10	Missing
Miss Sylvia Pankhurst	July 8	July 12	--
*Miss Mary Richardson	"	"	July 17
Mrs. Mackworth	July 11	July 16	—
Mrs. Wyan	July 15	July 18	—
Mrs. Rigby	On Remand	(1) July 16	July 17
		(2) July 22	—

* Arrested on another charge.

† Sentenced, on July 12, while out on licence, to three weeks.

Kitty Marion became a militant suffragette as a reaction to the abuse women were expected to endure if they wanted a career in the music hall. Determined to fight back, she was often first in line to volunteer for the most daring acts of arson across the country. In the weeks leading up to August 1913, she torched the pavilion at Hurst

Park Racecourse, was arrested and imprisoned, released under the Cat and Mouse Act, re-arrested on July 12th for breaking Home Office windows and finally released on July 17th. Her arrests sparked a backlash, including the planting of a bomb at the Lyceum Theatre in Taunton. Significantly this had the words 'Votes for Women', 'Judges Beware', and 'Martyrs of the law' painted on its sides. Sir Albert de Rutzen would have been well advised to take note.

The events that sent shock waves across North Devon, began late in the evening of Monday 3rd August when flames were spotted rising from Hollerday House, as reported by the *North Devon Journal:*

> It was 11.10pm to the minute on Monday when the first alarm of the outbreak was given. At that time PC Sparkes ... was in the square at Lynton. Hearing a woman shout near by, he looked up and at once saw that Hollerday House was on fire. The constable sent a man to call ex-constable Bibbings, who promptly summoned the Fire Brigade, and meanwhile hastened up to Hollerday. At first sight it seemed as though a chimney in the tower end was on fire, but closer inspection showed that the staircase under the tower was ablaze. Shortly afterwards PC Sparkes observed another distinct fire on the ground floor in the centre of the mansion so that there were two fires raging separately at the same time in different parts of the house ... Whilst inspecting the building and rendering all the help possible PC Sparkes found the scullery window at the rear of the mansion open and it is supposed that the incendiary entered the building by this window.

> … As time went on floor after floor collapsed in the mansion, the flames rising to a tremendous height, and the noise at times caused by falling timber and masonry was deafening. The heat was terrific, and at some point the workers could not approach the fire within a distance of fifty feet. Finally the remaining portions of the roof collapsed…

On the hunt for an exclusive, the paper's representative quizzed Mr Slee, the caretaker, over a newspaper report that two ladies had obtained the keys to the house on the Monday with a view to watching the sunset from the upper rooms.

> Mr Slee gave this report an emphatic disclaimer, and indirectly suggested that an incident on Sunday had given rise to this report. He went on to explain that on Saturday two American ladies (who had been staying at one of the local hotels) called at the Lodge and asked to be allowed to inspect Hollerday, and they accordingly were conducted over the mansion by him the next morning. The ladies expressed delight with Hollerday and announced their intention of communicating with the London agents with the view to purchase. The same evening the ladies went up to Hollerday grounds to see the sun set, and he saw them leave by way of the Lodge entrance a little later. He had never allowed the keys out of his possession and the last time the ladies in question were in the house was Sunday morning. He (Mr Slee) had definitely ascertained that these ladies left Lynton for Ilfracombe on Monday morning.

American? Potential purchasers? Perhaps. But there may be another interpretation.

'Ready?' the shorter of the two[we will call her Mary] adjusts her hat and drapes her coat over her arm. A little irregular but it is such a fine day.

'Oh, yes.' The taller of the two ladies [we will call her Kitty] has been dozing in the lobby of the Valley of the Rocks Hotel, gathering her strength. Four weeks on hunger strike has left her weak, despite the Blathwayts' ministrations at Batheaston.

'Remember, people can be very curious in the country. They may be suspicious.'

'And all they will find is two ladies in love with this glorious Devon Scenery and hoping to spend vast amounts of money on a mansion that has proved unsellable. We'll be welcomed with open arms.'

They step out into the narrow lane. Mary touches Kitty's arm, nodding towards the Stables opposite. 'Marie took a look at those.'

'Too many buildings close by, we can't risk it.'

'The second option is just up here.' Mary walks on.

'Wait, what's that?' Kitty points to their right.

'A funicular. It travels between Lynton and Lynmouth. Another bequest from George Newnes.'

'Is there anything he didn't pay for round here?'

Mary smiles. 'Not a lot! Take the town hall.' They pause outside a black and white timbered building towering over the street.

'Look more at home in the Swiss mountains. So another gift of the great and good George Newnes?'

'Yes, to celebrate Frank Newnes coming of age.'

'Now that is interesting.'

'Follow me.' Mary leads the way up the side of the building. 'There.'

'What am I looking at?'

'That shaft,' she points to the back of the building. 'Marie investigated it a while back. It leads to the heating apparatus.'

Kitty studies the shaft, then turns to scan the neighbouring buildings. 'Still too close.'

'Then on to our third option.' Mary points at the summit of the hill where Hollerday House stands sentinel over the village. 'The currently unoccupied country retreat of Frank Newnes MP.'

Kitty smiles. 'Excellent.'

They stride up the lane beside the town hall to the Lodge. Kitty raps on the door. A man in late middle age opens it, wiping his chin with his hand. 'Mr Slee?' she enquires.

'The very man. Good morning, Ladies. How can I help?'

'I understand you are the caretaker for Hollerday House.'

'Indeed I am. The finest house around these parts, though a little neglected having been empty for some years, since Sir George died. Tragic that, Tragic. Such a well-respected gent.'

'A matter of opinion,' Kitty whispers under her breath.

'Mr Frank has done a fine job but his heart's gone out of Lynton. The house needs some life breathing into it.'

'That is why we are here. We have an appointment.'

'Yes, of course. I'll be with you by and by.' Mr Slee disappears inside and returns with his jacket and cap proudly in place ready to escort these genteel ladies over the house and grounds. He'll do his best for Mr Frank, pointing out the charms of the house in its heyday. 'I'll go on ahead and open up. You take your time, it's a bit of a drag.'

Kitty and Mary stroll up through the cutting towards Hollerday House, pausing at the bend to catch their breath and take in the view of Countisbury Hill.

'Stunning,' Mary remarks. 'No wonder he chose to build here.'

'Little good that it did him,' Kitty responds.

'It's this way.' Mary pulls away and strides up the track.

'Wait up, Mary.'

'I'm sorry. How long on hunger strike this time?'

'Four weeks.'

'Four! You shouldn't be here. You could wait at the lodge. I can do what needs to be done.'

'What! And miss out on the fun? This is a perfect chance to communicate with our esteemed government. Wouldn't miss it for the world.'

'Look, up there.' Mary points to their right. Just visible is a stone rotunda and a parapet capping the seemingly endless facade of the building. 'I heard it was magnificent but this is …'

'Perfect.'

'Perfect?'

'Cricket pavilions, signal boxes - small fry. But this … this will send a message they can't ignore. That **he** *can't ignore.' There's passion in Kitty's voice.*

'We have to be prepared for a backlash, for harsher sentences. No-one's better placed than Sir Albert De Rutzen for that.'

'Let him do his worst. We are equal to it, Mary, you know we are.'

'We are, but what about the women here - Marie, Anne, all the others?'

'Marie has made her position clear. But there won't be any evidence against them will there? And we will be long gone.'

'She did the planning, showed herself here. Even declared herself a militant ready to do whatever was needed.'

'I've no doubt that she will. We have to keep Mrs Newby close to the fold. She will be very useful. But now, we have work to do.'

Later that night, as the flames took hold, a car was spotted travelling at speed along Lee Road from the direction of the Valley of Rocks heading east. It would have taken a confident driver to negotiate the dark streets so fast, perhaps a chauffeur? Perhaps someone who could also offer a bolthole close at hand. Peace Cottage, Vera Holme's home with Evelina at Brendon, was only a few miles away. Evelina was opposed to the WSPU's involvement in arson so it's doubtful she would have agreed to harbour the women. But her mother was critically ill so she may well have been away caring for her, leaving Vera free to make her own decisions.

While the community in Lynton was absorbing the shock of the destruction of Hollerday, the conspirators at Peace Cottage may have been looking to maximise their impact. The Devon and Somerset Staghounds were about to hold their opening meet at Cloutsham. It always attracted large crowds - and the women would pass close by on their way back to Bristol. It was too good an opportunity to miss. As readers of the local paper were soon to discover:

SOMERSET HILLSIDE ABLAZE
HUGE TONGUES OF FLAME.

> The opening meet of the Devon and Somerset Staghounds at Cloutsham attracted a large concourse of people and a sensational incident occurred in connection with this meet. Early in the afternoon, smoke was seen rising from the western

> side of Dunkery, 1,000ft above sea level, and directly facing The Ball at Cloutsham and the woods in which the hounds were at work. In an incredibly short time a large tract was ablaze and, fanned by a stiff breeze, flames swept up the hillside laying waste one side of Joan How, a minor peak, and sweeping then towards the Beacon that marks the summit. Huge tongues of flame swept like waves beneath the dense volume of smoke which arose from the hillside and cast a blur upon an otherwise radiant sky. A big staff endeavoured to cope with the fire but the lurid glare from Dunkery promised a long and difficult task. This outbreak is generally believed to be the work of Suffragettes, the women having been seen through the glasses close to the spot where the fire broke out.

And the women were not done yet.

> LARGE RICK FIRE.
>
> In consequence of every horse in the neighbourhood having been engaged for the meet (at Cloutsham) the Williton fire brigade were unable to respond to an urgent call to a large rick at Stringston eight miles distant ... The burning rick contained quite 100 tons of hay and there was another almost as large close by for which grave fears were entertained.

Stringston is on the road from Dunkery to Bridgwater, en-route for Bristol.

Lynton and Lynmouth were alive with rumours in the days following the fires, some with more substance than others. In one interview, Sir Thomas Hewitt, of the neighbouring property sounded very authoritative. 'Sir Thomas Hewitt ... stated that there was no question in his mind that the fire was the work of suffragettes. Three of his gardeners distinctly heard a series of explosions, followed in each case by flames ... "This seems clearly the result of the suffrage craze" said Sir Thomas "and everyone in Lynton is of the same opinion."' A credible view given everything we now know of the build up to these events, but Sir Thomas's involvement adds an interesting dimension. Unknown to the WSPU, just a few weeks before the fire Sir Thomas Hewitt purchased the freehold of Hollerday House. Frank Newnes was no longer the owner, simply the leaseholder. It was Sir Thomas who sustained the bulk of the loss not Frank Newnes, not the outcome the WSPU had conspired for.

But Hollerday was just one incident of many. The following year the Morning Post published a table listing all those properties completely or partially destroyed by arson. It demonstrated the scale of the suffragettes' campaign over twelve months, an escalation that had a massive financial impact - with losses of £380,000, the equivalent of just under £40 million today.

Date	Locality	House	Est. Loss
1913			
Mar. 19	Englefield Green	Lady White's	£2,300
Apr. 4	Chorley Wood	Roughwood	£2,500
7	Norwich	The Chase	£2,000
15	St. Leonards	Loveleigh	£5,000
May. 9	Barrow	Oak Lea	£6,000
10	Dundee	Faringdon Hall	£10,000
14	Folkestone	The Highlands	£500
18	Cambridge	Ridings	£850
June 4	Bradf'd-on-Av'n	Emscross	£7,000
10	East Lothian	Residence	£2,500
20	Olton	Residence	£1,000
30	Balfron	Balikinrain Castle	£25,000
July 4	Sutton Coldfield	Residence	£3,000
7	Rivington	Bung'low	£20,000
Aug. 4	**Lynton**	**Hollerday**	**£9,000**
22	Edinburgh	Residence	£300
26	North Finchley	Friern Watch	£500
Sept 12	Sutton	Residence	£500

Oct. 6	Hampton	The Elms	£1,500
26	Slough	Residence	£1,000
27	Bramshott	Mill House	£1,000
28	Bradford	Shirley Manor	£5,000
Nov. 11	Bristol	Begbrook	£4,000
23	Bath	Bathford	£3,000
Dec. 5	Wemyss Bay	Kelly House	£27,000
21	Cheltenham	Alstone Lawn	£350
1914			
Jan. 24	Lanark	Bonnington	£1,200
Feb. 4	Perthshire	Aberuchill Castle	£3,000
4	Comrie	House of Ross	£3,000
4	St. Filans	New Villa	£1,000
27	Redlynch	Residence	
Mar. 12	Ayrshire	Robertlawn	£15,000
27	Belfast	Abbeylands	£20,000
Apr. 9	Carrickfergus	Oxlands	£10,000

Numerous other attempts were made to burn dwellings at Beckenham, Hampstead, Potter's Bar, Hendon, Cooden Beach, Cardiff, Birmingham, High Wycombe, Bangor, Ardington, Jesmond, East Finchley, Tonbridge, Liverpool, Loughton, Willesden, Bedford, Salisbury, Shandon, Hanworth, Lisburn, Belfast, Dundee and Market Harborough. It's a daunting, or an impressive, count depending on your point of view. Either way, it split the WSPU and public opinion.

Unlike the close call when Lloyd George's house was destroyed, in Lynton someone had actually been hurt. Alfred Berry, a fireman, fell thirty feet off a ladder. He only sustained bruising and a sprained ankle but his injuries could have been much worse; perhaps the final straw for Evelina Haverfield. Her loyalty to the WSPU had been stretched to breaking point when the Pethick-Lawrences were expelled. Having now been complicit in lives being put at risk on her doorstep it was time for a complete break. She withdrew from the Paddington branch of the WSPU, removed herself from the speakers' list and followed the Pethick-Lawrences to a new organisation, the United Suffragists, formed by supporters who remained disillusioned by the lack of success of the NUWSS but who disapproved of the arson campaign of the WSPU. Alongside Emmeline and Frederick Pethick-Lawrence, Evelina discovered another familiar face from North Devon swelling the ranks of the United Suffragists, the previous candidate for the Barnstaple constituency, Henry Harben.

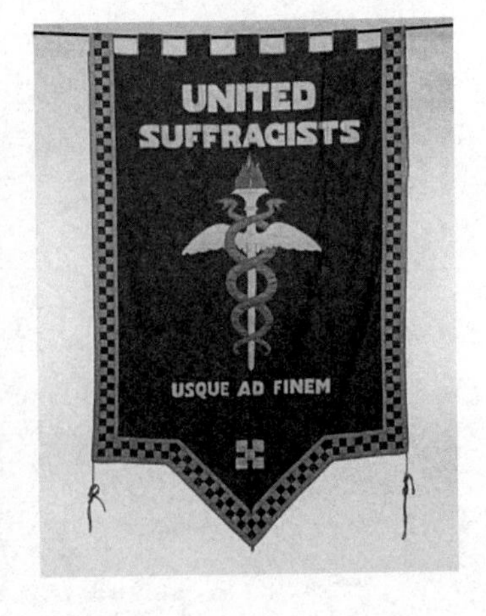

However, the Ilfracombe group was unwavering in its loyalty to the WSPU. Just days after the destruction at Lynton they launched their holiday campaign, recruiting visitors to sell *The Suffragette* on the streets - a brave strategy considering the inevitable local backlash. George Newnes was Lynton's hero. To destroy this last link with him was outrageous! Undeterred, the group entered a parade of pony carriages in the Ilfracombe carnival. One was decorated in the colours of the Tax Resistance League, undoubtedly Anne Ball's work. Another, protesting against the Cat and Mouse Act, attracted large crowds whenever it stopped.

Interest was so great they completely sold out of copies of *The Suffragette,* although the positive interest may have been down to a cunning advertising strategy. An endearing eight-year-old daughter of one of the group wove through the crowd selling the newspaper.

Marie Newby also had no intention of lying low. She was back in her trademark position by the archway in Ilfracombe High Street, unmissable in her WSPU apron, selling *Votes for Women*. This was a staggering display of her convictions. Here was a lady of standing in the community - surgeon's wife and pillar of the church - now a common street seller. A courageous and very public stand, particularly given the public reaction to the burning of Hollerday as reported in the North Devon Herald. 'For two or three weeks past there has been a good deal of talk about the suffragettes staying in the place but no one thought they would make a serious attempt at Lynton. Now, however, dire vengeance is being vowed upon them, several people stating they would execute all manner of punishment upon the suffragettes if only they could lay hands on them. Revolvers were freely spoken of, and people stated that they would not hesitate to use them whenever the occasion should arise!'

SUFFRAGETTES AT ILFRACOMBE.

Mrs. du Sautoy Newby selling the paper

Chapter Twenty-One
A Moderate Momentum
Autumn 1913 into Summer 1914

The NUWSS capitalised on the backlash against militancy in North Devon after Hollerday, extending their reach with a meeting in North Molton. The chair, Mrs Clunn, declared herself delighted that the first meeting with a suffrage bias ever held in North Molton was so crowded. The speaker, Miss Rochford, obviously inspired the group;

the vicar's wife was prompted to write: 'the audience were all awareness and have been discussing what they heard ever since'.

The NUWSS was also growing in the south of the county with reports of healthy meetings in Budleigh Salterton, Newton Abbot, Ottery St Mary, Plymouth, Tiverton, Topsham, Torquay and Totnes. Most of these groups, including Bideford and Barnstaple, were represented at the annual meeting of the South West Federation of the NUWSS in Exeter. It had been an exceptional year and for once this group of moderates could revel in the success of their own headline grabbing event - The Great Pilgrimage; they had a lot to celebrate.

Things were less harmonious in Ilfracombe, as reported in the November edition of the Gazette:

SCENE AT WOMEN'S LIBERAL MEETING

> At the opening of the annual meeting of the Ilfracombe Women's Liberal Association a painful exhibition was given of the extent to which the Liberal Party Women are still blinded to the vital issues. Mrs Baker, wife of the prospective candidate for the Barnstaple Division was addressing a meeting when a lady who had once been a member of the association, rose to protest against the treatment of women by the Government. A great uproar followed and the lady who had interrupted was compelled to leave the meeting to which she had not been invited.

Apparently all was forgiven and forgotten by the Liberal ladies after the spat with their blatantly anti-suffragist candidate. They applauded talk of 'the wonderful work accomplished by the Government' and the 'high tribute paid to Mr Lloyd George'. The one exception was Margaret Eldridge who couldn't contain herself. 'I rise to protest against the forcible feeding ...' Her voice was drowned out by women shouting, 'Sit down,' 'Go outside,' and 'Put her out.' Having owned up to no longer being a member of the

Women's Liberal Association, she was ejected from the meeting. Mr Baker expressed the wish that: 'even if some ladies have grievances he hoped they would be rectified in the equality of Mrs Baker's sharing with him responsibility, when the electorate of this Division elected him as their representative in Parliament.'

Margaret took to the newspaper to have the last word. 'I fear Mrs Baker, however charming she may be, will not do as a substitute for the vote, which despite the pessimistic views of the President of the Women's Liberal Association, will soon be given to us. She thinks we must spend our time and energy educating the dear little boys because it will be years and years and years before we win the vote for ourselves!'

It was a spirited repost and one which, according to the next local report in *The Suffragette,* injected new life into the Ilfracombe WSPU. With their only imminent plan being for a jumble sale in the autumn, they were in need of something to counter the inevitable anti-climax after the drama of Hollerday House.

Meetings continued, the next at Anne Ball's to hear Amy Montaque, chair of the Exeter WSPU. The subject was serious but they may have persuaded her to offer a taster of a performance she was due to give two days later at the 'Forest of Christmas Trees' fete to be held at the Barnfield Hall in Exeter. Together with her daughter she was performing, 'A chat with Mrs Chicky', a comic duologue where an anti-suffrage canvasser (Mrs H) is bested by the charwoman (Mrs Chicky) she seeks to convert:

> Mrs H (addressing Mrs Chicky): 'The fact is that a few women who haven't got anything else to do have some ridiculous idea that they ought to have votes, and do men's work instead of their own and interfere with the government of the country, and if you and I and millions of other women who know better don't stop them at once we shall simply have England going to rack and ruin.'

Her assumptions of the ignorance and obedience of the working woman are gradually eroded by Mrs Chicky:

> 'I'm not saying this 'ere votes goin' to set everythin' right, but I do say as anythin' that's done without it'll be just patchin' an' nothin' more! It's goin' to make women *count*! It'll make 'em 'ave to be reckoned with! ... I believe same as you do that the men want to do what's best for us, but - you 'ave to be a woman yourself to know where things 'urt women! It's Gawd's truth, that is, an' I say Gawd bless the ladies 'oo are 'elpin' us by stickin' out for it!'

The end of the year saw a rallying call to the WSPU across Devon. Mrs Pankhurst had evaded prison under the Cat and Mouse Act by sailing to America for a speaking tour. She was now due into Plymouth on the liner 'Majestic' and word was that she would be re-arrested. Plans were made to wait in a boat out in the bay and smuggle her off the ship and up to London. But the police got to her first and she was taken to Exeter prison, precipitating a flurry of violence. Pillar-boxes were vandalised, windows smashed and there was an outbreak of fires including at a timber yard at Devonport.

In Exeter prison, Emmeline Pankhurst immediately went on hunger and thirst strike, prompting a vigil by suffragettes outside. It was a courageous choice. A rowdy crowd physically assaulted the suffragettes, prompting a rescue by prison warders. Undeterred, the suffragettes kept up their vigil, whether by the prison walls or in cars close by. Curious crowds gathered from time to time, the perfect opportunity for a speech by suffragette, Elizabeth Grew. 'We are doing what a member of your cabinet told us to do. Mr Hobhouse said there was no popular demand behind the woman's claim, such as men showed when they burnt down Nottingham Castle and a great part of Bristol to get their vote. If the only popular demand this Government will recognise is that of burning buildings, it's going to get it.'

Ilfracombe WSPU welcomed in 1914 with a well attended 'At Home' for working women at the 'Elite'. Anne, Margaret and Marie spoke with their usual enthusiasm on the need for the vote and for militancy. It's a message that continued to go down well in Ilfracombe but this militant group were increasingly becoming an island surrounded by the more moderate suffragists making headway across the rest of North Devon.

In Barnstaple the NUWSS was going from strength to strength, now boosted by the support of Miss Rosalie Chichester from Arlington Court. In January she hosted a non-militant pro-suffrage meeting as well as chairing a local meeting. Ruth Giles, an organiser with the SW Federation, was the speaker this time, focusing not only on women's growing wish for more responsibility but the need to address wider issues such as their working conditions.

Monthly meetings continued in Barnstaple with Ruth Giles back in February and another significant figure in the movement, Miss Muriel Matters, booked for March. An Australian born suffragist, Muriel Matters was a member of the Women's Freedom League and in the unique position of being the only woman to visit North Devon who actually had the vote. She was an eloquent and forceful speaker and unanimously carried the motion, 'That this meeting asks for a Government measure to enfranchise women'.

Ruth Giles also took up the gauntlet of promoting the NUWSS in Bideford. Despite growing support, public meetings were still a bit of a gamble, particularly given the town's anti-suffrage reputation. But, as she stood to address an audience of over 700, most seemed eager to listen.

However, not everyone was happy. A Mr Edes wrote to the Bideford Gazette to vent his outrage:

> It was the duty of the speakers to show that the Union they represent came before the public with clean hands, to point to instances in which the Societies concerned had denounced and reprobated the senseless and cruel outrages which have been inflicted on all classes by the hysterical hooligans who glory in

> the debasement of their sex as a means of attaining the vote… The inherent wickedness and folly of the acts themselves have not been condemned, but emphasis has been laid on the bad tactics of the law-breakers in exasperating public opinion. So might a man denounce dishonesty on the ground that is does not pay.

There was a flurry of activity when Sheffield-based suffragist Mrs Whalley arrived to speak in Landkey and at Westbank in Bideford. She appealed to the working men of her audience. How could it be right that every class of man was represented in Parliament, yet half the community were still needing and asking for representation? The following day, she took advantage of a crowd gathered on Bideford quay, keen to spot the aeroplane piloted by French airman Henri Salmet. He was due to stop off on his promotional tour around the West Country on behalf of his sponsor, the *Daily Mail*. Mrs Whalley's trademark stirring speech provided a welcome diversion as they waited.

Mrs Whalley's appearance was part of an extended NUWSS caravan tour around the remote parts of the West Country. Devon stops included Holsworthy, Black Torrington, Torrington, South Molton, Chulmleigh, Lapford, North Tawton, Okehampton, Bridestowe, Lydford, and Tavistock. As a publicity stunt it was remarkably effective with hundreds of copies of the *Common Cause* sold en-route. And it was the catalyst for some active canvassing in South Molton by Miss Frost, Mrs Smart and Miss Baly. Like many societies before and since, the NUWSS took a stall in the market, the 'means of doing much excellent propaganda work.' The ladies were able to field questions from the general public, with one man showing a

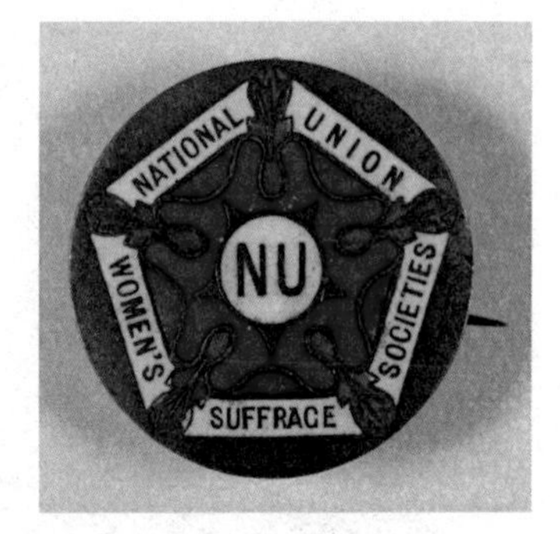

particular interest. It was only later they discovered he was the Liberal agent!

All the activity was proving very effective. A grand total of 478 societies and 52,000 members were now part of the NUWSS, a stark contrast to the 2,000 signed up to the WSPU. Although many stayed loyal, the splits brought about by Christabel's policy of expulsions inevitably had an impact on the already small membership.

But Ilfracombe WSPU was planning a major attraction to boost numbers. Flora Drummond had agreed to speak as part of a country-wide tour. Flora, or General Drummond as she was known, had been a key worker with the WSPU since 1906 and the success of the numerous processions and demonstrations were down to her organising flair. On this tour she was booked at Oxford Assembly rooms, Brighton Dome and, finally, Ilfracombe Town Hall. Members set about publicising her arrival. A pony-cart was decorated and driven around the town on the Saturday prior to the meeting: volunteers were recruited to hand out flyers, steward the meeting and sell copies of *The Suffragette*. All was in place. But as the pony cart was making its way around Ilfracombe harbour, General Flora Drummond was being marched away from a protest in Hyde Park under arrest. It was the end of her speaking tour.

It was a massive disappointment for the Ilfracombe group. They rarely attracted such a high profile speaker to this rural outpost. But the WSPU was nothing if not resourceful. Within hours another speaker was found. The meeting would go ahead, but with Miss Barbara Wylie. 'Who?' was probably the response. Suffragists in Canada could have provided the answer. In the summer of 1912 Barbara Wylie interviewed the Canadian Prime Minister, then on a visit to London. Premier Borden stated he had no intention of introducing legislation giving votes to women but he would be happy to receive any deputation from women in Canada to lay their views before him.

When he returned to Canada, Barbara followed. She made quite an impression at the Montreal Council of Women. 'Miss Barbara Wylie ... is a tall, really beautiful looking woman with every appearance of refinement and intelligence above the ordinary. She spoke intelligently of the suffrage movement, explaining the larger significance of the demand for votes for women and what she called "the absolutely unjust, cruel and disgraceful conduct and trickery" of the Asquith government." She spoke as a highly intelligent woman burning with the conviction that her cause was right. She also showed plainly a spirit of resolute intention not to give up the fight for a minute until the battle had been won.'

She made such an impact she nearly caused a riot. The Montreal Gazette reported: 'The address given by Miss Barbara Wylie ... called up such unexpected warmth from the audience, for and against militant methods, that only the decision of the President prevented the two parties from locking horns and deciding the question then and there.' The Toronto Daily News described her as a: 'tall, intellectual, aristocratic looking Englishwoman with the real thing in the way of accents and a Made-in-England hat. A stone thrower and a hunger-striker by her own admission, the militant missionary would throw with precision and strike after due consideration.' She lived up to her reputation as a rogue militant by urging the women of Canada to 'use whatever weapons were placed in their hands and fight for their rights.'

Back in England, her forthrightness was an act of rebellion too far. Three months later she was arrested and imprisoned for openly advocating acts of militancy and violence. Now actively campaigning again, she was an immediate draw for the crowds in Ilfracombe. It was the ideal opportunity to promote sales of Christabel's recently published book *The Great Scourge and How to End It*. It was an interesting decision. The book concentrated on a subject that was becoming an obsession with Christabel; sexually transmitted diseases and how sexual equality (votes for women) would help the fight against these diseases. It was a justified exposé but came across as a moralising, anti-men stance that proved too much for Charles Gray and other pro-militancy members of the Men's Political Union. The group was wound up in 1913 when relations with the Pankhursts became 'exceedingly trying.'

It was the last in a long series of major splits involving the WSPU. The first resulted in Charlotte Despard and others leaving to form the Women's Freedom League. The next was the fundamental rift with the Pethick-Lawrence's and finally the expulsions of Sylvia and Adela Pankhurst.

By contrast, the NUWSS had grown steadily over twenty-three years with no splits and little dissension. Local organisers would come and go - in North Devon, Mrs Lightbody had now taken over in Bideford and Mrs Hastle in Instow - but essentially it displayed remarkable unity under the leadership of Millicent Fawcett. She remained firmly convinced that the militants were harming women's chances of gaining the vote by alienating MPs and the public.

The WSPU begged to differ. Throughout the spring of 1914 militancy continued to escalate both locally and nationally. In May, they decided to take their appeal to the King at Buckingham Palace, an encounter witnessed by suffragette, Kate Parry Fry and recorded in her diary:

> Thursday, May 21st 1914
> ... In the afternoon I went to Buckingham Palace to see the Women's deputation - led by Mrs Pankhurst - which went to try

and see the King. It was simply awful - oh! those poor pathetic women - dresses half torn off - hair down, hats off, covered with mud and paint and some dragged along looking in the greatest agony. But the wonderful courage of it all. One man led along - collar torn off - face streaming with blood - he had gone to protect them. Fancy not arresting them until they got into that state. It is the most wicked and futile persecution because they know we have got to have 'Votes' - and to think they have got us to this state - some women thinking it necessary and right to do the most awful burnings etc in order to bring the question forward. Oh what a pass to come to in a so-called civilised country. I shall never forget those poor dear women.

The militants continued to make headlines in North Devon:

8th June	Newquay tennis courts disfigured with 'Votes for Women' written on the grass
17th June	Fire at Lynton Town Hall. White room enveloped in flames
18th June	Churches in North Devon closed to visitors in fear of outrages by suffragettes
22nd June	Bideford Bowling Pavilion destroyed by fire
22nd June	Persistent rumours of Suffragettes visiting Westward Ho! golf links
26th June	Lynton foreland lighthouse still closed in consequence of so many suffragette outrages

Meanwhile the NUWSS quietly extended its influence. On July 20th, Miss Hedge held an open-air meeting in George Nympton and a week later they were back at the Assembly Hall in South Molton with Miss Shapcott of Ashmill in the chair. Talks on *The History of the Women's Movement* and *The Vote as a Symbol of Freedom* inspired thirty-one women to join up, and there was enthusiasm for forming a group in the town. But within days, talk of freedom was to have a very different resonance.

On August 4th, 1914 Great Britain declared war on Germany. Winston Churchill described the scene in London:

> It was eleven o'clock at night – twelve by German time – when the ultimatum expired. The windows of the Admiralty were thrown wide open in the warm night air. Under the roof from which Nelson had received his orders were gathered a small group of admirals and captains and a cluster of clerks, pencils in hand, waiting. Along the Mall from the direction of the Palace the sound of an immense concourse singing 'God save the King' floated in. On this deep wave there broke the chimes of Big Ben; and, as the first stroke of the hour boomed out, a rustle of movement swept across the room. The war telegram signalling, 'Commence hostilities against Germany', was flashed to the ships and establishments under the White Ensign all over the world. I walked across the Horse Guards Parade to the Cabinet room and reported to the Prime Minister and the Ministers who were assembled there that the deed was done.

Christabel's reaction was characteristically controversial: 'War is God's vengeance upon the people who have held women in subjection and by so doing destroyed the perfect human balance.' But she quickly declared that the WSPU would abandon its campaigns and support the British government. *The Suffragette* was reborn as *Britannia* as the Pankhursts adopted an increasingly nationalistic, even jingoistic stance, handing out white feathers to young men who failed to volunteer.

Millicent Fawcett was more considered in her support for the war effort, recommending the NUWSS suspend suffrage propaganda and focus on relief work: 'Let us show ourselves worthy of citizenship, whether our claim to it be recognised or not.' While some continued to lobby for the vote throughout the war, Millicent was more circumspect: 'There is no forecasting what effect the present war may have on the position of the suffrage question … it is also highly probable that the general isolation and status of women in the eyes of the general public will not be improved. At any rate, we should be ready for all emergencies, ready to restart our suffrage campaign at the first opportunity.'

Four years later she had her answer.

AT LAST!

Reproduced by kind permission of the Proprietors of "PUNCH," from the cartoon of January 23, 1918, and published by the National Union of Women's Suffrage Societies, 62, Oxford Street, W. 1.

Chapter Twenty-Two
Votes for Women
February 1918

In February 1918, the war achieved what years of campaigning had failed to - votes for women.

But it was a potential crisis over male voters that started the ball rolling. Only men resident in the UK for twelve months prior to a general election were eligible to vote. At a stroke, thousands of servicemen risking their lives for their country were disenfranchised. Something had to be done. In 1916 an inter-party committee was formed to discuss franchise reform. This Speakers' Conference Committee, as it became known, was chaired by the Speaker of the

House of Commons, James William Lowther, the same man who had ruled against the women in 1913. It didn't bode well.

But, in a startling about-turn, Asquith gave a speech to the Commons that implied he was relaxing his opposition to women's suffrage. Why the change of heart? According to Asquith it was to recognise the vital wartime role of women. Over 700,000 were employed in munitions factories. Thousands more worked on farms, in the docks, government departments and other male-dominated industries such as engineering. Not to speak of the huge increase in women in more traditional working roles as typists and secretaries. More than ever women realised they could function as well as men. It was something they wouldn't forget once the war was over.

Asquith knew that when the men returned, women would be ousted from roles that had given them confidence, independence, new skills and an income. They would be made redundant or forced back into domestic work - creating a fertile recruiting ground for the suffragettes. It would be a flashpoint for a return to, as Asquith put it 'that detestable campaign that disfigured the annals of political agitation in this country'. The escalation of militancy before the war divided the suffrage movement. Many thought it did more to hinder than advance the cause. But the prospect of a return to that militancy inevitably played a part in Asquith's about-turn. How could he imprison and torture women who had made such a valuable contribution to the war effort? The last thing society needed now was massive social unrest.

On October 12th, the thirty-four members of the Committee began their deliberations. Women across the country held their breath. Under a headline of 'Is It Victory At Last?' *Votes for Women* considered wildly varying rumours that on the one hand claimed woman suffrage would be omitted altogether, and on the other confirmed that the majority of the Committee were in favour.

At least the press had finally made up its mind:

> There will be great disappointment among men of progressive views if the Committee fail to come to any agreement on the

question of women's suffrage ... This grievous defect will have to be remedied by a courageous government. *Daily Chronicle*.

If it is true that the Speakers' Conference, while dealing with many questions of registration and franchise, has failed to come to an agreement on woman suffrage, that fact is the gravest possible setback to the cause of justice and reform. *The Herald*.

No great measure of electoral reform would be tolerable, or could be tolerated, without it. *Manchester Guardian*.

The days before the report was published were an anxious time for suffrage societies, finally united under the banner of the National Council for Adult Suffrage. They inundated the government with resolutions: 'that the war has made obsolete all our past system of enfranchisement and registration. That the only solution of the difficulties that have arisen is adult suffrage, including women.' *Votes for Women* entered the fray with a barbed reminder of past promises. In an editorial directed at the Prime Minister, no longer Herbert Asquith but Lloyd George, it commented: 'It is not forgotten how he [Lloyd George] "torpedoed" the Conciliation Bill because its franchise was not broad and democratic enough ... now is his golden moment.'

In reality, women's suffrage was very much on the Committee's agenda. In a measure of how far attitudes had changed they considered awarding women an equal franchise with men. But to create a female majority was a step too far. They compromised with a recommendation that the franchise should be limited to women over the age of either thirty or thirty-five. This was the proposal presented to Lloyd George in January 1917.

Two months later, twenty-two suffrage societies, under the leadership of Millicent Fawcett, met with Government ministers for a briefing on the recommendations of the Speakers Conference. The women made their dissatisfaction clear. The proposal still fell short of their demand for the vote on the same terms as men, a double blow given that the voting age for servicemen was being reduced to nineteen. But compromise was inevitable. They agreed to support a Bill if the age limit for women was lowered to thirty.

A few weeks later, in a moment of sublime irony, Herbert Asquith stood in the House of Commons to move that a Bill be introduced in accordance with the Speakers Conference recommendations. The Bill achieved a massive majority at its first reading, 341 votes to 62. Support was undiminished at the second reading and on June 19th 1917, the Commons approved the women's clause by 387 to 57 votes.

The *Manchester Guardian* said it all: 'Women, and not a few select women, but women in their millions, will vote at the next election to be held in this country. That is a tremendous event.'

The question has to be asked. Asquith's about-turn was one thing but why did the overwhelming majority of men in the House of Commons rush to support the suffragist cause? The wartime Coalition Government helped. An all-party agreement on women's suffrage removed the fear that one party might benefit from the enfranchisement of women. But many nurtured another agenda, believing a limited franchise would keep the suffragists happy while delaying the more radical reform of full and equal voting rights for men and women for years to come.

Conservative Party support for the Bill was rooted in expediency. Their research revealed that 98 out of 142 constituencies supported votes for women. If this was true of the whole country, then the party faced heavy election defeats if it did not support the enfranchisement of women.

Whatever their reasoning, the war made it easier for MPs to give ground without losing face. They weren't giving in to violence, but recognising the valiant efforts of a group of people who were helping the nation through a crisis. Over eight million women were now on the cusp of achieving what thousands had fought and suffered for.

The Representation of the People Act 1918, given Royal Assent on the 6th February, gave the vote to all men over twenty-one, or nineteen if in service in the war, and every woman of thirty or over who was a member or married to a member of the Local Government Register, a property owner, or a graduate voting in a University constituency. The 7.7 million citizens entitled to vote in 1912 leapt to 21.4 million, with women making up about 43% of the electorate.

But the majority of women who had contributed so much to the war effort, many risking their lives in munitions factories, were young and single - the very women still denied the vote. Some saw this as a betrayal, leaving them second-class citizens. This political inequality remained the status quo for ten more years until the Equal Franchise Act of 1928 finally gave women the vote on the same basis as men, bringing the number of women eligible to vote up to 15 million.

For most though,1918 was a watershed. Millicent Fawcett declared it the greatest moment in her life. A victory party was held by suffragist societies at the Queen's Hall in March, and November saw the icing on the cake when the Parliament (Qualification of Women) Act 1918 was passed. Women could now not only vote but stand for election as an MP. The following year a woman stepped inside the Houses of Parliament - not to lobby, to plead or to cajole,

but to take her place as an equal among men. That woman was Nancy Astor, representing the constituency of Plymouth Sutton, Devon. She was nominated by Mabel Ramsay and owed a great part of her emphatic victory on polling day to the work of the ladies of the NUWSS.

Nancy Astor made history as the first woman to take her seat in Parliament but she wasn't the first to be elected. That honour goes to Countess Markiewicz, an aristocrat's daughter from Southern Ireland. Born Constance Gore-Booth, she first dipped her toe in the women's suffrage movement in her twenties. She joined the NUWSS and, together with her sister, Eva, organised the Sligo Women's Suffrage Society, the third in Ireland. It was the time of her first recorded speech: 'Now, in order to attain to any Political Reform you all know that the first step is to form societies to agitate and force the government to realise that a very large class have a grievance, and will never stop making themselves disagreeable till it is righted. John Stuart Mill said thirty years ago that the only forcible argument against giving women the suffrage was "that they did not demand it with sufficient force and noise". Silence is an evil that might easily be remedied, and the sooner we begin to make a row the better.'

It wasn't long before her beliefs translated into political activism. In 1908 a sympathy with the suffrage cause led her to Manchester to help Eva and fellow suffragette Esther Roper fight Churchill's re-election. She made her mark driving an old fashioned carriage drawn by four white horses through the crowded streets. When a male heckler asked her if she could cook a dinner, she responded: 'Yes. Can you drive a coach and four?'

In 1912 she supported a suffragette demonstration to demand an amendment of the Home Rule Bill to include women voters, the first of its kind to be held in Dublin. She also joined Irish suffragettes parading with posters when Asquith visited. As in England, the women were attacked by a mob and several, including Constance, were hurt. But while Constance admired the suffragettes and lent her support, she believed they should be aiming higher – for complete freedom not just the vote. She became increasingly drawn to the charismatic figures calling for Irish independence. She befriended Helena Molony and Anna Catherine Parnell and became a fervent supporter of Sinn Féin, an organisation that embraced women in senior positions on its executive from the very beginning.

Journalist Desmond Ryan painted a picture of her: 'Madame De Markeivicz sat in the middle of the room, pensive and beautiful with a costly lace collar draping her shoulder, ready to explode into the most unconvincingly blood thirsty sentiments as the lecture and debate developed but speaking with a gentle charm to anyone who approached her in private. She was, although her fury expressed in such polite accents had a comic aspect, a very courageous woman, for she had broken with all her friends and immediate circle to champion an obscure movement.'

During the 1916 Easter Rising Lieutenant Markievicz, as she became, was in the thick of the fighting, wounding a British army sniper. At her court martial she was sentenced to death, commuted to life in prison on account of her sex. She was held in Aylesbury Prison for a year, before being released in 1917 as part of a general amnesty.

At the 1918 general election, Constance Markievicz was elected as the MP for the constituency of Dublin St Patrick's, emphatically beating her opponent and, just two years before Ireland was divided, becoming the first woman ever returned to the Commons at Westminster. But as a member for Sinn Féin she did not take her seat, leaving Nancy Astor to take that step into history just a year later.

Marie Newby remained loyal to the WSPU and the Pankhursts, continuing to hold meetings in Ilfracombe until 1918. The organisation disbanded at the end of the war but the Pankhursts' connection with North Devon remained. Westward Ho! had become a firm favourite with the suffragettes, a relationship cemented by the WSPU when they bought Manorville, where Emmeline Pankhurst stayed for several months before leaving for America in 1920.

The Representation of the People Bill received Royal Assent on February 6th 1918, a month that also saw the last edition of *Votes for Women,* the journal the Pethick-Lawrences had kept going since their split with the Pankhursts. It had chronicled the movement since October 1907 but now was to close, with any regrets 'overwhelmed by the joy and thankfulness we feel at the victory of our cause.'

Frederick Pethick-Lawrence reflected on the long struggle:

> Ten and a half years ago! Not very long in the life of an individual; still less in the list of a nation. But to women, what a chasm between then and now.
>
> Ten and a half years ago men assumed, and the great mass of women accepted the assumption, that men were the race, that men's point of view was the right point of view, that democracy meant the rule of men, that women were inferior and subject. Into most men's minds today there has come a doubt as to the truth of this assumption, into most women's minds there has come a certainty that it is false.
>
> Ten and a half years ago this paper was founded as the organ of a little body of people who with eyes of faith saw what is seen now by the multitude. Those were days when … merely to believe in votes for women was to be a crank. While for those

who went further ... and dared to act on this conviction, the penalty was to become the object of general derision.

Different temperaments produce different actions ... The conciliatory suffragists placed their entire confidence in argument and persuasion. The militants ... flung themselves on the prejudices of the age with the vigour and determination of youth. Many things went under in the struggle - 'ladylike' reserve, old ideas of womanly dutifulness and wifely obedience, implicit confidence in those in high places, respect for the laws of the land. Thousands made the acquaintance of prison cells ... they explored the rottenness of the established order and exposed the truthlessness of officialdom alike in the prison and in the highest positions in the State.

This paper supported from the first the militants, and became the recognised organ of one great section [WSPU]. The years that followed were packed full of incident. Great public meetings, monster demonstrations, 'raids' on Parliament, ejections from Cabinet Ministers audiences, police court proceedings, sentences in prison, welcomes on release, hunger strikes, forcible feedings, followed one another with startling rapidity. A series of Suffrage Bills were introduced into the House of Commons and suffered their demise. Pledges were given by statesmen and shamelessly broken. Passions rose and methods of violence succeeded mere defiance of the law.

Division and separations came with the suffrage movement ... But looking back on the whole story of the agitation one is struck with the value of the contribution supplied by each section of the movement ... The war which changed all Europe changed incidentally the character of the struggle for the suffrage ... several suffrage societies put up their shutters ... This paper, and the organisation to which it had then become attached [United Suffragists] stuck womanly to their purpose.

Marie Newby, Anne Ball, Margaret Eldridge and all who fought alongside them, would surely have agreed whole-heartedly with the final editorial in *Votes for Women*.

> We do not know what the future will contain for the new men and women voters ... Looking back over the years, seeing the magnificent sacrifices that have been offered up in the cause of women's freedom, we have no fears as to the use that will be made by women of their votes, working side by side with the men whose citizenship they now share. With our faces set to the future, we greet, for the last time through the pages of *VOTES FOR WOMEN*, all those who have travelled with us to the great day which sees the dawn of women's freedom.

National Timeline

1832:

- First women's suffrage petition to Parliament
- Great Reform Act - confirmed the exclusion of women from the electorate by defining voters as 'male persons'

1851: Sheffield Female Political Association submits a petition to the House of Lords calling for women's suffrage

1865: Society for the Promotion of Women's Suffrage formed in Manchester. Elizabeth Wolstenholme-Lemy - secretary.

1866: John Stuart Mill petitions Parliament for a female franchise based on a property qualification

1867:

- Second Reform Act – male franchise extended. Attempts to replace use of 'male person' with 'person' fails
- National Society for Women's Suffrage is formed

1869: Municipal Franchise Act. Single women ratepayers now able to vote in local elections

1870: The Married Women's Property Act allows married women to retain ownership of their own property

1870-1883: Several Women's Suffrage Bills introduced but defeated each time, often by Gladstone

1884: Third Reform Act – Male electorate doubled to five million; women again excluded

1886-1892: Three further Bills are introduced but defeated

1889: Women's Franchise League campaign for the vote for married as well as single or widowed women

1894: Local Government Act puts married women on same footing as widows and spinsters - eligible for election as Poor Law Guardians and as Parish and District Councillors

1896: National Union of Women's Suffrage Societies (NUWSS) is formed: President - Millicent Fawcett

1902: Women's textile workers from Northern England present a 37,000 signatory petition to Parliament demanding votes for women

1903: Women's Social and Political Union (WSPU) founded in Manchester by Emmeline Pankhurst with daughters Christabel and Sylvia

1905:

- Militancy begins with the first arrests and imprisonment of Annie Kenney and Christabel Pankhurst
- 'Deeds not Words' adopted as campaign slogan
- Daily Mail labels women 'Suffragettes'
- Women's Franchise Bill, introduced by Keir Hardie, talked out

1906:

- First deputation to Parliament led by Mrs Pankhurst
- WSPU opens its headquarters in Clements Inn, London

1907:

- NUWSS Mud March – largest open air demonstration ever held (at that point) – over 3000 women took part
- March from first Women's Parliament to Westminster to protest at omission of votes for women from King's speech results in brutal treatment of women and 54 arrests
- Under the Qualification of Women Act, women now eligible to vote in and stand for election onto, borough and county councils
- Women's Freedom League, (WFL) led by Charlotte Despard, founded after split with WSPU over Pankhursts' autocratic leadership
- Another Women's Suffrage Bill talked out at second reading
- Deputation from second Women's Parliament - 75 arrests
- Women's Anti-Suffrage League and Men's League for Opposing Women's Suffrage formed

1908:

- Private Members' Suffrage Bill carried by 271 votes to 92 at second reading. Further progress is blocked
- Elizabeth Garrett Anderson first woman selected as mayor
- Mass London procession and Hyde Park rally - estimated 300,000-500,000 attend
- First window-smashing campaign in Downing Street in response to police brutality

- Kitty Marion, the WSPU's most destructive professional travelling militant, becomes involved with the WSPU
- NUWSS repudiates military action
- Helen Ogston is labelled 'The Woman with the Whip' after a protest at a Liberal meeting

1909:

- Marion Wallace Dunlop first hunger striker – released after 91 hours of fasting
- 108 women arrested after a WSPU-organised window breaking action after 8th Women's Parliament
- Women's Freedom League picket the House of Commons
- Women's Tax Resistance League founded. No taxation without representation
- First force-feeding of hunger strikers in English prisons
- Mrs Pankhurst and Evelina Haverfield in court to invoke the 1869 right to petition the King. Case is presided over by Sir Albert de Rutzen, father-in-law of Frank Newnes

1910:

- General election. WSPU campaigns against Liberal candidates in 40 constituencies but Asquith is re-elected
- Cross-Party Conciliation Bill is introduced including a limited franchise for women
- WSPU suspends militancy
- Conciliation Bill passes its 2nd reading by a majority of 110 but Asquith refuses it more parliamentary time
- WSPU deputation turns bloody. Becomes known as Black Friday because of police brutality. Over 100 arrested, plus almost 150 in the following week
- 1910-1912 - More Bills introduced but none are passed

1911:

- Women boycott the census
- Women's suffrage organisations come together for a massed Coronation Procession

- Asquith introduces a Government Suffrage (Reform) Bill - ostensibly capable of amendment to include women but the WSPU is sceptical
- militancy (deputations and window-smashing) is renewed - 220 are arrested

1912:

- Mrs Pankhurst announces an intensification of militancy
- Mass window-smashing action in the West End and Whitehall. 121 arrested
- Police raid WSPU HQ. Christabel flees to Paris
- Conciliation Bill is defeated
- Christabel Pankhurst begins arson campaign
- Government introduces Reform Bill - women are not included
- Mr & Mrs Pethick-Lawrence split from the WSPU - unhappy about militant tactics
- Mrs Pankhurst intensifies militancy, inciting rebellion
- WSPU begins to destroy contents of letterboxes

1913:

- Speaker's ruling wrecks inclusion of women in Reform Bill
- Unprecedented militancy, tightly controlled and instigated by the leadership. Mansions burnt, including Lloyd George's house, art work and golf courses vandalised, telephone wires cut, dummy bombs left in public buildings
- Start of intense period of arrests and imprisonment of WSPU leaders including Mrs Pankhurst
- The Prisoners' Temporary Discharge for Ill Health (Cat and Mouse) Act is passed - hunger-strikers released to prevent deaths in custody then re-arrested when recovered
- Emily Davison dies after being trampled at the Derby
- NUWSS organise nationwide Pilgrimage ending with mass meeting in Hyde Park

1914:

- Sylvia and Adela Pankhurst are expelled from the WSPU
- Mary Richardson slashes the Rokeby Venus painted by Diego Velázquez in the National Gallery

- Mrs Pankhurst leads last militant deputation to Buckingham Palace - worst violence of the campaign. 66 are arrested
- Police raid WSPU Headquarters
- 4 August: Britain declares war on Germany
- All suffragette prisoners are released. WSPU campaigning ceases immediately while others continue suffrage work

1916:

- Suffrage organisations debate Government's proposed changes to electoral register to enfranchise servicemen
- Asquith now supports the enfranchisement of women
- Speakers' Conference formed to report on electoral reform

1917: Conference recommends limited women's suffrage

1918:

- The Representation of the People Act enfranchises women over 30 provided they, or their husband, meet a property qualification. About 8.4 million women gain the vote
- Under the Parliament (Qualification of Women) Act women can now stand for Parliament
- Women vote in a general election for the first time

1918: Constance Markiewicz becomes the first woman to be elected to Westminster but as a Sinn Féin MP does not take her seat

1919: First woman MP to take her seat, Nancy Astor, enters the Commons

1928:

- Representation of the People Act enfranchises all women aged 21 and over
- Millicent Fawcett attends Parliament to see the vote take place
- Emmeline Pankhurst dies just a month before the Act comes into force

Local Timeline

1870: First suffragist petition from North Devon, an area strongly liberal and non-conformist, comes from Barnstaple
1870-1908: 253 petitions in favour of Women's suffrage presented to Parliament from Devon
1871: Millicent Fawcett tours Tavistock, Plymouth, Devonport and Exeter
1881: Meeting in support of female suffrage organised at Ilfracombe by three men
1886: Suffrage petition from Ilfracombe Conservative Association
1887: George Newnes' first visit to Lynton at invitation of Thomas Hewitt
1893: Hollerday House completed. Family spend each August, September and Christmas there
1900: George Newnes elected Liberal MP for Swansea until retired due to ill health in 1910
1907:

- Annie Kenney appointed WSPU organiser for the West of England
- General election - Mrs Pankhurst and Annie Kenney campaign against Liberal in Newton Abbot

1908:

- Mary Phillips released from Holloway. Joins Annie Kenney, Elsie Howey, Gladice Keevil, Clara Codd and Mary Blathwayt in the WSPU West of England campaign
- Mrs Pethick-Lawrence and Annie Kenney at Plymouth Guildhall

1909:
January

- Debate on Woman's Suffrage at Ilfracombe organised by YMCA. Speech by Adela Pankhurst
- Debate on Woman Suffrage at Barnstaple YMCA. Overwhelming vote in favour of Women Suffrage

February

- Plymouth & Torquay WSPU activity
- Mrs Pankhurst addresses meetings in Torquay and Plymouth

March

- Plymouth & Torquay holding monthly meetings
- Open air meeting in Dartmouth
- Hon Mrs Haverfield speaks in Sherborne. Hon Sec of new group here
- WSPU meetings in Penzance, Paignton, Weston-Super-Mare

April

- WSPU Shop opens in Plymouth & Torquay
- WSPU organisers :
    - Vera Wentworth – Plymouth
    - Elsie Howey – Torquay & Paignton
    - Annie Kenney – Cardiff
    - Mrs Dove Wilcox – Bristol
- Weekly WSPU 'At Homes' in Plymouth
- Open air WSPU meetings in Dartmouth, Paignton, Totnes & Teignmouth

May

- Mrs Montagu of Crediton speaks at Torquay WSPU

June - Whitsun

- WSPU demonstration planned in Plymouth
- Jessie Kenney, Elsie Howey & Vera Wentworth challenge Prime Minister Asquith at Clovelly Court
- Mrs Pankhurst and Evelina Haverfield in court to invoke 1869 right to petition the King. Case is presided over by Sir Albert de Rutzen, father-in-law of Frank Newnes
- George Newnes' fortune has gone, squandered on ill-judged investments. Bad health, a drinking problem and a "failing mind" contribute to his problems

July

- Miss Rind leads WSPU holiday campaign in Ilfracombe
- First WSPU meetings in Tavistock and Torre
- WSPU organisers:
    - Mary Blathwayt and Vera Wentworth at Plymouth

    - Mary Phillips covering Ilfracombe and Swansea from her base in Penzance
- WSPU now holding open-air meetings at Devonport Dock Gates, Plymouth Saltash, Torquay Strand, Plymouth Market Square and St Marychurch

August

- Mary Phillips, Elsie Howey and Vera Wentworth arrested at Exeter. Sentenced to 7 days' imprisonment
- WSPU Meetings in Dawlish, Torquay, Paignton and St Marychurch
- Exeter WSPU meetings held daily in anticipation of Earl Carrington's visit
- Miss Vera Holme makes her first appearance as chauffeur to the WSPU

September

- WSPU holiday campaign in Ilfracombe conducted by Miss Mari Pearce and the Inglis sisters
- WSPU meeting in Exeter to hear Exeter hunger strikers
- Reception at Torquay to welcome Miss Elsie Howey after her hunger strike

October

- New WSPU campaign opened at Weymouth in Dorset Evelina Haverfield in the chair – speakers Annie Kenney and Miss Brackenbury
- Campaign extends to Wellington, Street and Bampton
- Weekly 'At Homes' commence at Barnfield Hall, Exeter
- Willey's, Exeter - speech by Miss Vera Wentworth

November

- WSPU meetings in Torquay, Exeter, Crediton and Ilfracombe - with Helen Ogston (Lady with the Whip)

December

- Helen Ogston speaks at Barnstaple
- Kate James speaks against militancy in Barnstaple
- Mrs Pankhurst arrives in Plymouth from America

- Judges decide against Mrs Pankhurst and Mrs Haverfield in the case relating to the Right of Petition
- WSPU meetings:
  - Exeter group visit Bampton for the first time
  - Public Meeting in Barnstaple with Miss Ogston
  - Polling day in Torquay. Decorated trap and car driven around the constituency
  - Meetings in Yeovil, Wellington and Street with Evelina Haverfield in the chair
  - WSPU organisers:
    - For the South West - Miss Annie Kenney
    - For Exeter - Miss Dugdale

1910:

January

- Winston Churchill dispatched to West Country to bolster the election campaign
- WSPU Exeter Election Campaign boosted by Gladice Keevil - they oust the Liberal candidate
- Sir Ernest Soares (Liberal) returned for Barnstaple
- Annie Kenney draws unprecedented crowds in Bridgwater (Possibly 10,000) - Conservative victory
- 7 Liberals unseated across the West Country
- Miss Keevil speaks at Runnacleave Hall, Ilfracombe
- Barnstaple 'At Home' with Helen Ogston

May

- Death of the King

June

- George Newnes dies at Hollerday aged 59. Frank Newnes inherits extensive debts
- Devon suffragists and suffragettes travel from Exeter to take part in the Great March in London on June 18th

August

- Ilfracombe launch holiday campaign supported by Helen Craggs - first suffragette imprisoned for arson

- Women's Suffrage meetings held in the Strand, Barnstaple. Meetings advertised in chalk on pavements. Speakers - Mrs Mackworth & Miss Pridders
- Anna Parnell moves in at 6 Avenue Rd, Ilfracombe to lodge under the name of Cerisa Palmer

September

- Annie Kenney draws crowds at Axminster, Seaton, Lyme Regis and Sidmouth and Ilfracombe

October

- WSPU militants first meeting at Marie Newby's -, St Mary's, Broad Park Avenue, Ilfracombe. Meeting addressed by Annie Kenney
- Local WSPU society formed with Miss Newby as secretary, Nurse Anne Ball as literary secretary
- Lady Isabel Margesson speaks in Exeter and Ilfracombe

November

- Should the Parliamentary Franchise be extended to women? debated at Braunton Literary Debating Society. Small majority against
- WSPU and NUWSS both campaign in Mid Devon as Asquith calls another election
- NUWSS have branches established in Exeter, Sidmouth, Teignmouth, Ottery St Mary, Topsham, Torquay and Plymouth
- WSPU tactics succeed in Torquay, Mid Devon, Tavistock and two Plymouth seats as the Liberals are all ousted

December

- Women's Freedom League operate out of premises in Torquay for the election

1911:

February

- Correspondence to North Devon Journal on Woman Suffrage by SUUM CUIQUE.
- WSPU meetings at the Imperial, Barnstaple and Gaiety Hall, Ilfracombe. Speaker - Mr Pethick-Lawrence.

- Devon societies in the NUWSS
    - Exeter - Sec Miss Montgomery
    - Sidmouth - Sec Lady Lockyer
    - Teignmouth - Sec Miss Allen
    - Three towns & District - Sec Dr Mabel Ramsay
    - Topsham - Sec Mrs Frood

April

- Anne Ball refuses to pay taxes. Goods seized at Ashleigh Rd Nursing Home, Barnstaple
- Anne Ball opens up Barnstaple nursing home for census evaders
- Annie Kenney speaks at an Ilfracombe WSPU meeting, part of 3 month campaign including Exeter, South Molton and Dulverton
- New members include a 95 year old lady
- North Devon Journal includes Table of Suffrage Societies submitted by SUUM CUIQUE
- Sir Ernest Soares resigns forcing a by-election in the Barnstaple constituency
- Sir Godfrey Baring, Liberal candidate, gives first speech in Ilfracombe
- Taunton branch of NUWSS now well established

May

- Marie Newby and Evelina Haverfield interview election candidates at Bideford and Appledore
- NUWSS organiser, Marguerite Norma-Smith, campaigns in Lynton, Coombe Martin, Ilfracombe, Bideford, Appledore and Barnstaple
- Frank Newnes speaks in support of Sir Godfrey Baring
- Sir Godfrey did not vote on the 2nd reading of the Women's Suffrage Bill (carried with majority of 167)

June

- NUWSS organiser, Marguerite Norma-Smith, forms a Barnstaple Society - a year after Ilfracombe WSPU is formed
- Also Bideford with Joanna Preston–Whyte as secretary

- And Appledore with Miss E. Martin, Torridge House as Secretary. 51 attend first meeting
- Ilfracombe join women from Bristol, Bath, Bridgwater, Cornwall, Crediton, Devizes, Exeter, Honiton, Paignton, Plymouth and Torquay to swell estimated 40,000 in the women's Coronation Procession in London
- Coronation of George V

July

- Hollerday fails to sell. Family left with enormous debts
- Ilfracombe WSPU offer 'At Homes' attracting new members
- Marie Newby campaigns in the West Somerset by-election alongside Annie Kenney, Mrs Pankhurst, Evelina Haverfield and Vera Holme
- Marguerite Norma-Smith campaigns for the NUWSS from her headquarters at Taunton

August

- Anne Ball arranges a daily WSPU stall in Ilfracombe market during the election followed by a weekly Saturday stall through the season

September

- Mrs Nash wins a prize in Bideford carnival for her WSPU decorated bicycle
- Anna Catherine Parnell, using the alias of Cerisa Palmer, drowns off the Tunnel beaches, Ilfracombe
- Annie Kenney leaves as WSPU West Country organiser
- Ilfracombe WSPU organise weekly sewing work-parties
- Sir Godfrey Baring entertains 2,000 Liberal Women at Upcott

November

- Asquith introduces Manhood Suffrage Bill with no provision for women
- Marie Newby travels to London to join the protests

December

- Miss Davenport takes over local organisation of the NUWSS launching a new group in Barnstaple

- WSPU meeting at Gaiety Hall, Ilfracombe. Speakers - Mrs Montague, from Exeter, and national activist, Jessie Smith
- A1 motors run a trip to Bath to hear Lloyd George

1912:

January

- Miss Davenport from the NUWSS holds meetings in Barnstaple, Bideford, Instow, Northam and Appledore

March

- Marie Newby imprisoned in Holloway after taking part in a window-smashing campaign in London
- Marie Newby on hunger strike
- Tax-Resistance Sale of goods seized from Anne Ball, at Barnstaple. Previous sale in Ilfracombe
- Christine Wodehouse from Bratton Fleming (cousin of PG Wodehouse) now Barnstaple NUWSS organiser
- Mrs Baring-Gould ill - Sir Godfrey to stand down

June

- Marie Newby opens WSPU meeting at the Gaiety Ilfracombe with statement on her imprisonment
- Georgina Brackenbury, speaker, imprisoned with her

July

- Newly appointed prospective Liberal Candidate, Henry Harben, resigns in protest at force-feeding

August

- Meeting at Braunton's Cross Tree re Women's Suffrage
- Ilfracombe launch holiday campaign with support of Dr Christine Murrell, GP from London

October

- H.A.Baker adopted as new Liberal candidate - confirmed anti-suffragist
- Barnstaple meeting with Miss Abadam, Rev Hatty Baker and the Rev G.H. Davis

November

- Evelina Haverfield and Marie Newby interview Sir Godfrey Baring at the House of Commons

1913:

January

- NUWSS active in Sidmouth

February

- Christine Wodehouse Barnstaple NUWSS secretary
- Women's Liberal Association challenge H.A.Baker on his anti-suffrage stance - without success
- Correspondence on militancy in the Ilfracombe papers

March

- Olive Wharry from Holsworthy, a retained WSPU militant, is sent to Holloway prison for 18 months for setting fire to the tea pavilion at Kew Gardens
- Wharry is released under Cat and Mouse Act having lost over two stone after hunger striking for 32 days
- Marie Newby writes to paper on the need for militancy

April

- Suffragettes open a shop in Church Street, Ilfracombe
- Ilfracombe WSPU launch a series of weekly debates

May

- Suffrage meeting at Ilfracombe

June

- Church League for Women's Suffrage meeting at Ilfracombe. Organiser is Marie Newby
- Ilfracombe WSPU send a cross of flowers in the colours to the funeral of Emily Wilding Davison
- NUWSS meetings held in Bideford and Barnstaple
- NUWSS Pilgrimage sets out from Land's End

July

- Up to 7,000 spectators greet the Pilgrimage in Exeter
- WSPU meeting at Anne Ball's. Speaker, Miss Mary Phillips (one of the Exeter hunger strikers) on militancy
- Police patrol GWR line from Tiverton Junction to Hele overnight after telegram received from militants
- Suffragette bomb found at Taunton theatre

August

- Arson of Hollerday House - attributed to Kitty Marion
- *Times* headline "DEVON MANSION DESTROYED BY FIRE - SUPPOSED SUFFRAGIST OUTRAGE"
- Report in *North Devon Herald* of suffragette activity in Lynton with one lady promising militancy
- Sir Thomas Hewitt recently purchased the freehold of Hollerday. Frank Newnes simply the lessee. Loss, estimated at £10,000, only partly covered by insurance
- Fire in heather on Dunkery Beacon
- Haystacks on fire at Stringston
- Reports of suffragette activity in North Devon
- Barum Chief Constable issues a warning to be vigilant
- Sir Thomas Hewitt blames suffragettes for Hollerday

September

- NUWSS meeting in North Molton
- NUWSS growing in South Devon with regular meetings in Budleigh Salterton, Newton Abbot, Ottery St Mary, Plymouth, Tiverton, Topsham, Torquay and Totnes

November

- Margaret Eldridge protests at, and is ejected from, Ilfracombe Women's Liberal Association meeting
- NUWSS meeting in Marine Hotel motor garage, Instow
- Seaton carnival includes 'Forcible Feeding' Tableaux includes doctor, warder, nurse and two suffragettes

December

- Mrs Pankhurst is arrested on disembarking boat from America at Plymouth
- suffragettes hold vigil outside Exeter prison

1914:

January-March

- Ilfracombe WSPU meetings continue
- NUWSS meetings at Barnstaple now chaired by Miss Rosalie Chichester

- NUWSS speakers address meetings in Bideford, Instow, Barnstaple and Landkey
- NUWSS launch a caravan tour around Devon including Holsworthy, Black Torrington, Great Torrington, South Molton, Chulmleigh, Lapford, North Tawton, Okehampton, Bridestowe, Lydford, and Tavistock
- NUWSS take a stall in South Molton market

April

- Flora Drummond's engagement to speak at Ilfracombe cancelled after she is arrested in London
- Replaced by Barbara Wylie, the 'militant missionary'

May

- Large gathering in South Molton for NUWSS meeting

June

- Newquay tennis courts vandalised with 'Votes for Women' written on the grass
- Lynton foreland Lighthouse closed due to suffragettes
- Fire at Lynton Town Hall
- Several churches in North Devon closed to visitors in the fear of outrages by suffragettes
- Bideford Bowling Pavilion destroyed by fire
- Persistent rumours of suffragettes at Westward Ho! golf links

July

- Morning Post includes Hollerday House in list of suffragette arson attacks. Cites loss as £9,000
- NUWSS hold meetings in George Nympton and South Molton

1914-1918:

- The Pankhursts speak in Devon in support of the war effort

1916:

- Millicent Fawcett speaks to Exmouth branch of NUWSS

1918:

- Marie Newby remains loyal to the Pankhursts', continuing to hold meetings in Ilfracombe

1919:

- Manorville, Westward Ho! bought by the WSPU
- Nancy Astor is the first woman to take her seat in Parliament, representing Plymouth Sutton constituency

1920:

- Emmeline Pankhurst stays at Manorville before travelling to America

1928:

- Death of Emmeline Pankhurst in the very week that all women achieve the vote

1950s:

- Remains of Hollerday House blown up as commando training exercise

1952:

- Stone from Hollerday House is used to rebuild the bridges in Lynbridge and Barbrook following the Lynmouth Flood Disaster

Illustrations

Sources

Atkinson, Diane, *The Suffragettes in Pictures* (The History Press, 2010)
Bearman C.J., *An Examination of Suffragette Violence* (English Historical Review, April 2005)
Boyce, Lucienne, *The Bristol Suffragettes* (Silverwood 2013)
Bradley, Katherine, *Friends & Visitors: A First History of the Women's Suffrage Movement in Cornwall 1870-1914* (The Hypatia Trust, 2000)
Christie, Peter, *A North Devon Chronology. The Heritage Album. 175 years in Devon (1824 -1999)*
Colmore,Gertrude, *Suffragette Sally* (Broadview Press, 2008)
Cowman, Krista, *Women of the Right Spirit: Paid Organisers of the Women's Social and Political Union* (Manchester University Press: 2007)
Crawford, Elizabeth, *The Women's Suffrage Movement in Britain and Ireland: A Regional Survey*
Friederichs, Hulda, *The Life of Sir George Newnes*, 1911
Gray, Todd, *Remarkable Women of Devon* (The Mint press 2009)
Groves, Patricia, *Petticoat Rebellion* – The Anna Parnell Story (Mercier Press, 2009)
Joannou, Maroula, *The Women's Suffrage Movement: New Feminist Perspectives* (Manchester University Press: 1998)
Kenney, Annie, *Memories of a Militant* (E. Arnold, 1924)
Harrison, Shirley, *Sylvia Pankhurst: A Crusading Life 1882-1960.* Arum Press
Heathcote, Sally, *Suffragette* (Jonathan Cape, 2014)
Law, Cheryl, *Suffrage and Power: The Women's Movement 1918-1928*
Liddington, Jill, *Vanishing for the vote: Suffrage, citizenship and the battle for the census* (Manchester University Press: 2014)
Lytton, Constance, *Prisons and Prisoners, The Stirring Testimony of a Suffragette* (Virago, 1988)
Metcalf, A.E. *Women's Effort: A Chronicle of British Women's Fifty Years' Struggle for Citizenship 1865-1914* (Oxford: 1917)
Mackenzie, Midge, *Shoulder to Shoulder.* (Harmondsworth, 1975)

Pankhurst, Christabel, *Unshackled: The Story of How we Won the Vote.* Ed Lord Pethick-Lawrence (London: 1959)
Pankhurst, E. Sylvia: *The Suffragette Movement: An Intimate Account of Persons and Ideals* (Virago,1977)
Pankhurst, E. Sylvia, *The Suffragette: The History of the Women's Militant Suffrage Movement 1905-1910* (New York: 1911)
Pankhurst, Emmeline, *My Own Story; The Autobiography of Emmeline Pankhurst* (Virago, 1979)
Pugh, Martin,The Pankhursts/ Allen Lane, The Penguin Press
Purvis, June, *Emmeline Pankhurst: A Biography*
Raeburn, Antonia, *The Militant Suffragettes* (Michael Joseph, 1973)
Rosen, Andrew, *Rise up Women! The Militant campaign of the Women's Social and Political Union 1903-1914* (London 1974)
Sykes, Christopher, *Nancy. The Life of Lady Astor* (Granada, 1979)
Wilson, Gretchen, *With All Her Might* (Holmes & Meier, 1998)

Suffrage Newspapers

Votes for Women (WSPU 1907 -12), *Votes for Women* (Ed. Pethick-Lawrences' 1912-1914), *Votes for Women* (United Suffragists 1914 -1918), *The Suffragette* (WSPU 1912-1915)
Britannia (WSPU 1915-1918), *Common Cause* (NUWSS)
Free Church Suffrage Times, The Vote (WFL)

National Papers

Birmingham Daily Mail, Daily Herald, Daily Telegraph, Daily Express, Luton Times and Advertiser, Manchester Guardian, Manchester Courier, Newcastle Journal, The Morning Post, Times

Local Newspapers

Bath Courier and Weekly Gazette, Bath Chronicle , Bideford Gazette, Exeter & Plymouth Gazette, Exeter Flying Post, Ilfracombe Chronicle, Ilfracombe Gazette, North Devon Journal, North Devon Herald, Somerset & North Devon Gazette, Western Daily Mercury, West Somerset Free Press, Western Times, Western Morning News

Journals

History Magazine, Women's History Review, English Historical Review, Transactions of the Devonshire Association

Archives

Barnstaple Athenaeum, Bideford & District Community Archive, Braunton Museum, British Library, British Museum,Gloucester Archive, Ilfracombe Museum, Museum of London, The National Archives, Women's Library, LSE ,West Country Studies Library

Internet resources

www.britishnewspaperarchive.com
www.nationalarchives.gov.uk/archon
www.thesuffragettes.org
www.lucienneboyce.com
www.womanandhersphere.com
www.spartacus-educational.com
http://richardjohnbr.blogspot.co.uk/2008/04/women-get-vote-what-happened-during-war.html

The Power of Three
Thomas Fowler, Devon's Forgotten Genius

WOODEN COMPUTER INVENTED IN NORTH DEVON. A striking headline for a provincial newspaper. The article in the North Devon Journal continued "It is fascinating ... to know that one of the original pioneers of the computer was a self-taught bookseller and printer of Torrington who was born over 200 years ago. His name was Thomas Fowler." I was intrigued, especially given that Great Torrington is close to where I live. But surely 'the father of computing' was Charles Babbage? Who was Thomas Fowler?

It was a question that was to take me on an emotional journey, from excitement at this charismatic inventor's early success to despair at his betrayal, from admiration of his ingenuity to the agony of obscurity. Despite an initial reluctance to peer over the precipice into the world of mathematics and the history of computing, I knew this was a story that had to be told.

My first searches revealed nothing. Then I met local businessman, John McKay, who had discovered a brief biography of Fowler. It depicted an extraordinary, self-taught mathematician and inventor who transformed himself from fellmonger to successful businessman and pillar of the community. A significant achievement in itself; but more was to come — much more. Thomas Fowler invented a unique calculating machine. Not something that would normally inspire me, but this was different. His absolute belief that this invention would be his claim to fame leapt off the page. So why had I never heard of him? Had his invention survived? If not, did any drawings exist? Could it be recreated?

Curiosity and a nagging need for justice launched me on a search for clues, most of them buried deep in the archives of the most respected scientists of the nineteenth century. Along the way I discovered an unexpected fascination with the leaps of imagination that lie behind the birth of the modern computer. All leading to one startling conclusion.

The computer is an indispensable part of daily life. We rely on it to communicate, for entertainment and for access to a wealth of resources that our bookshelves could never hold. Yet many of us are ignorant of the processes that make all this possible — with one exception. It is well-known that the technology relies on the binary number system, a choice made by early computer scientists that dominates the world of computing. But a fundamentally different path might have been taken more than a century earlier had the pioneering work of this humble, self-taught mathematician been adopted.

For a while there was every chance that it would. Yet after a flurry of recognition, Fowler's work was consigned to obscurity. Why?

This book tells the fascinating story of a remarkable Devon man who was convinced that his innovative work was overlooked because of his humble origins and unorthodox path to mathematical brilliance. It includes a layman's view of Fowler's inventions and a full appendix containing his detailed mathematical deliberations and original source material for those who would like to explore further.

Thomas Fowler died in 1843 but the final chapter of his story has yet to be written. As twenty-first century scientists rediscover his ground-breaking work, perhaps there is still time for Fowler's dying wish to be fulfilled:

My greatest wish was to have had a thorough investigation of the whole principle of the Machine and its details as far as I could then explain them, in a way very different from a popular exhibition - this investigation I hope it will still have by some first rate Man of Science before it be laid aside or adopted.

"*Fowler's calculator was in certain respects vastly more promising than Babbage's.*"
Dr Doron Swade MBE, previously Assistant Director and Head of Collections at the Science Museum, London.

"*Computers might have changed history and our world almost a century sooner than they did had the ideas of Fowler been understood and adopted by Babbage.*"
Ralph Merkle, Senior Research Fellow at the Institute for Molecular Manufacturing, California, and co-inventor of public key cryptography.

For more information see www.boundstonebooks.co.uk.

Seeds of Doubt

On the evening of August 15th 1952 the worst floods ever to hit the west of England destroyed the beautiful coastal village of Lynmouth in North Devon. Newspaper headlines reflected the nation's shock at the scale of this tragic natural disaster. Page after page documented the devastation left behind when a series of torrential downpours caused the East and West Lyn rivers to burst their banks. Such was the force of the water that ten-ton boulders were carried out to sea; roads, bridges and entire cottages were swept away.

Thirty-four men, women and children lost their lives that night.

There is no doubt that this was a disaster: but a natural one? There are those who still believe that the events of that night were not so much an Act of God as an Act of Man. This novel blends fact and fiction in a story of one woman's struggle to expose those who contrive to manipulate one of the greatest powers on earth - the weather.

All references to official documents are factual and listed in the appendix. All organisations and characters, however, and the roles they play, are entirely fictional.

Reader Reviews

"I finished Seeds of Doubt last night. It was a great book... I loved the story, Ingrid's voyage and struggle, and the sense of Devon and history. The research struck me as particularly impressive... thanks for the entertainment of a great book." Simon Hall - Home Affairs correspondent BBC South West.

"…To build a conspiracy thriller on an event as well known as the Lynmouth flood disaster, and to make it both plausible and exciting, is no mean feat. The dialogue is well written and convincing and the plot is unpredictable with enough twists to keep any thriller reader happy."

"…I've just finished Seeds of Doubt; WONDERFUL. *I loved it; it has all the right ingredients - drama, tension, intrigue, love, secrets, danger and truth. Looking through the references, why hasn't this made more of a splash (unintended pun) in the national and local press? It's huge. Thank you so much for a thought provoking and thoroughly edge of the seat read."*

" … I couldn't put (it) down! It is an amazing story, vividly written... some of your insights and or descriptions are so 'word perfect' and then there are the subtle sub plots! The actual theoretical basis is very disturbing - terrifying? - and so it took some hours in the day to shake off from being inside the book. Remarkable. Brilliant! Thrilling. Enthralling…"

"…Just had to let you know that I REALLY *enjoyed your book – it is well written & constructed, and a very good read."*

"I thoroughly enjoyed this book. The way that fiction was blended with fact was very well done, and the list of references to the official documentation really makes you think … Have already bought this for friends!"

Shadow Child

Prologue

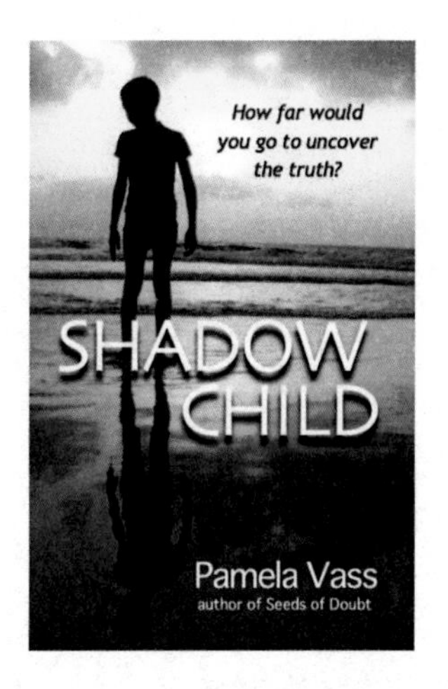

Paul gazed at the identically dressed women filtering through the door. He stared at each face in turn, searching for the look, the mannerism, the feature that would unlock the past. He remembered deep brown eyes, tumbling hair, a raucous laugh and slender fingers ... leaving their trace. He shivered. Sometimes his mind played tricks on him.

There were no physical characteristics to link him with any of them, not that he could see. Carol, the family liaison officer, gestured towards a slight figure with closely cropped hair, eyes cast down, walking towards them.

Carol nodded. 'Hi, Sonya. This is Paul.'

The woman lifted her head. 'You're taller than I thought.'

Paul removed his jacket and hung it over the chair, tweaking the folds until it hung freely - anything to fill the space created by sixteen years of not knowing. Finally, he snatched a glance at the woman sitting opposite him - his mother. 'Can't believe it's you,' he said. 'I'd have come, years ago. But they didn't tell me. The bastards all knew but no-one told me!'

She shifted in her chair, her eyes flitting from one side of the room to the other. 'What good would it have done?'

'Good? I'd have told them it couldn't have been you …'

'I'm not having this conversation.' She half rose.

'Paul knows that.' Carol sent him a warning glance. 'You agreed to fill in the gaps. He agreed to stick to that. Paul?'

He shrugged. 'Questions have been in here so long ...' he tapped his forehead.

Her face gave nothing away. 'So what do you want to know?'

The words welled up. 'What was it like? What was I like? I remember a caravan. Is that where we lived?'

'For a bit.'

'What did we do? What sort of a kid was I?'

'Christ, I don't know. It was years ago!'

'I don't think Paul's after anything specific, Sonya,' Carol mediated. 'Just something to help him fill in the gaps.'

She rubbed at an imaginary mark on the back of her hand. 'You used to go off round the site. You was always running off.'

'Why? I loved being with you. We were good, weren't we?' Silence. 'I remember we used to go to town.'

Sonya picked at a chipped fingernail. He let the silence hang. 'Yea, we used to go to town,' she said.

'All of us?'

'Mostly.'

'But sometimes just you and me, yeah?'

'Maybe, when you needed something, like trainers. You was always getting through trainers.'

'What did we eat? What was my favourite?'

She pressed her fingers against her forehead. 'I don't know ... fish and chips. Burger from the van.'

He'd tried, really tried. But he had to know. 'Why? Why did you say it was you?'

She looked at him now, for a fraction of a second, before pushing her chair back. 'Just a minute.'

'You're innocent ... I'll prove it,' Paul called, fighting the impulse to run after her, to wait by the door, to make sure this minute didn't last another lifetime.

Reader reviews

"Shadow Child is fantastic. You have such a gift for touching people's emotions."

"A very emotive & intriguing subject ... Your vast knowledge and experience of the subject really shine through and it is so well written."

"I could not put your book down; a great book."

"I read Shadow Child a little while ago. It was amazing…"

"I have just read Shadow Child. It was a brilliant read …"

About the Author

Pamela Vass was drawn to England's West Country forty years ago and only afterwards discovered a family tree firmly rooted in Devon soil. Since then it has provided much of the inspiration for her writing.

Pamela's career includes several years as Director of The Whodunnit Company, offering murder mystery events in the UK and abroad. Prior to this she was a social worker with Barnardos and two Social Services Departments. This professional experience provides a strong foundation for *Shadow Child*, a gritty and realistic depiction of the challenges faced by a child abandoned by his mother. He never gives up searching for her, not as a child, not as an adult. But the past casts a long shadow and his quest for the truth threatens his very future.

An interest in historical research led to *The Power of Three*, the story of a nineteenth century Devon inventor. Tragically Fowler's ground-breaking work on the principles that underpin the modern computer was lost, but a combination of Pamela's research and the expertise of an international team has reinstated him as a significant figure in computing history.

While organising murder-mystery weekends in Lynmouth, Pamela came across a rumour that outside agencies had played a part in the devastating floods of 1952. This led her to the National Archive at Kew and previously secret government documents that shed light on the events surrounding the disaster. In *Seeds of Doubt*, Pamela blends fact and fiction in a story of one woman's struggle to expose those who contrive to manipulate one of the greatest powers on earth - the weather.

Pamela continues to live and write in Devon, finding inspiration in its unique landscape and the stories it holds.

For more information see www.boundstonebooks.co.uk